LIFE AND TIMES
QUIZZES

First published in 2003 by Miles Kelly Publishing Ltd,
Bardfield Centre, Great Bardfield, Essex, CM7 4SL

ISBN 1-84236-274-7

2 4 6 8 10 9 7 5 3 1

Project Manager: Ruthie Boardman
Cover Design: Guy Rodgers

Contact us by email: info@mileskelly.net
Check our website and purchase other Miles Kelly products:
www.mileskelly.net

Printed in Italy

LIFE AND TIMES QUIZZES

by
Christopher Rigby

MILES KELLY
PUBLISHING

About the Author

Born in Blackburn, Lancashire in 1960, Christopher Rigby has been compiling and presenting pub quizzes for the past 15 years. When he is not adding to his material for quizzes, Christopher works in the car industry. He is married to Clare – they have two teenage daughters, Hollie and Ashley and share their home with two demented dogs called Vespa and Bailey. A keen Manchester United fan Christopher lists his heroes as George Best and Homer Simpson.

THE LIFE AND TIMES OF ... EXPLAINED

The following quiz book contains 90 different quizzes on a variety of different subjects. These are wide and varied and each quiz builds up a mini biography of the subject in the spotlight.

Below is an example:

The Life and Times of Hanna Barbera

The American animators Hanna and Barbera were born in 1910 and 1911 respectively and in 1937 created *Tom & Jerry* for MGM. Below are ten questions on the life and cartoons of Hanna Barbera.

1. Which cartoon feline, the indisputable leader of the gang, was voiced by Arnold Stang?
2. Which cartoon canine's name was lifted from a line from the Frank Sinatra song 'Strangers In The Night'?
3. Which Hanna Barbera cartoon series was set in the year AD 3000?
4. Which cartoon told of the trials and tribulations of the Boyle family?
5. Which song was Huckleberry Hound often heard singing?

The Life and Times of Clint Eastwood

Hollywood superstar Clint Eastwood was born in 1930 and after playing numerous bit parts in a variety of B movies he landed the lead role in the 1964 spaghetti western *A Fistful Of Dollars*. Below are ten more trivia titbits about the life of Clint Eastwood.

1. Of which American town did Clint become Mayor?

2. What was the title of the film that marked the directorial début of Eastwood in which he played a disc jockey?

3. In which TV western did he play the character of Rowdy Yates?

4. What is the name of the TV producer who he married in 1996?

5. For which 1992 film did Eastwood win a Best Director Oscar?

6. Name his co-star in the film, *The Outlaw Josey Wales* who he later married.

7. Where did Clint escape from in a 1979 film?

8. Who did Eastwood play in a series of films, including *The Enforcer* and *The Dead Pool*?

9. When Eastwood played the Good and Eli Wallach played the Ugly, who played the Bad?

10. What was Clint Eastwood's occupation in the 1993 film, *In The Line Of Fire*?

ANSWERS
1. Carmel 2. *Play Misty For Me* 3. *Rawhide* 4. Dina Ruiz 5. *Unforgiven* 6. Sondra Locke 7. Alcatraz 8. Harry Callahan AKA Dirty Harry 9. Lee Van Cleef 10. Presidential bodyguard

The Life and Times of Horatio Nelson

Horatio Nelson was born on September 29, 1758, the son of Reverend Edmund Nelson and his wife Catherine. Below are ten posers from the past on the life of one of history's greatest naval heroes.

1. At the Battle of Santa Cruz which arm did Nelson lose?

2. In 1799, Nelson began a notorious affair with whom?

3. In what year did Nelson die at the Battle of Trafalgar?

4. As Nelson lay dying which captain is he said to have requested a kiss from?

5. Which flagship of Nelson now stands in dry dock at the Portsmouth naval base?

6. How old was Nelson when he commanded his first vessel. Was he 15, 20 or 25?

7. According to the history books what were the last seven words spoken by Horatio Nelson?

8. Which actor played Nelson in the 1973 film, *A Bequest To The Nation*?

9. On January 9, 1806 which London building held the funeral of Lord Nelson?

10. A sniper from which ship fired the fatal shot that killed Nelson?

ANSWERS
1.The right arm 2. Lady Emma Hamilton 3. 1805 4. Captain Thomas Hardy 5. HMS Victory 6. 20 7. Thank God, I have done my duty 8. Peter Finch 9. St Paul's Cathedral 10. The Redoubtable

The Life and Times of Paul McCartney

Paul McCartney was born in Liverpool in 1942 and following the break-up of the Beatles in 1970 he formed his own band Wings. Below are ten rocking riddles on the life of this lovable moptop.

1. The cover of which Wings album featured a host of stars including Christopher Lee and Michael Parkinson?

2. Which Bond movie did Paul compose and perform the theme for?

3. Which 1977 Christmas hit featured the melodic harmonies of bagpipes?

4. What is the first occupation to be mentioned in the lyrics of the Lennon & McCartney composition 'Penny Lane'?

5. Which record producer was known as the fifth Beatle?

6. Who collaborated with McCartney on the song 'Ebony and Ivory'?

7. In 1980, McCartney was detained for eight nights in a prison after drugs were discovered in his airport luggage. In which country was he imprisoned?

8. On which track did Paul duet with Michael Jackson on the album, *Thriller*?

9. Which ex-member of the Moody Blues joined Paul and his wife Linda to form Wings?

10. Which Lennon & McCartney song that featured on the *Sergeant Pepper's* album became a hit single for Elton John?

The Life and Times of William Shakespeare

The playwright William Shakespeare was born in 1564 in a house in Henley Street, Stratford-upon-Avon. He died at the age of 52 and now lies at rest in a grave at Holy Trinity Church. Below are a barrage of brain-busters on the life and works of the Bard of Avon.

1. Which monarch sat on the throne of England when Shakespeare was born?

2. Which play includes in the cast a tinker called Snout, a joiner called Snug and a weaver called Bottom?

3. How many children did William Shakespeare have?

4. Which theatre built in 1599 was partly owned by Shakespeare?

5. Who played the young bard in the Oscar-winning film, *Shakespeare In Love*?

6. Which play opens with the line, 'For he tonight shall lie with Mistress Ford'?

7. Who did William marry on November 28, 1582?

8. What is the name of the Merchant of Venice?

9. Which Shakespeare play provided the inspiration for the 1953 musical, *Kiss Me Kate*?

10. Which four Shakespeare plays are collectively known as the four great tragedies?

ANSWERS

1. Elizabeth I 2. *A Midsummer Night's Dream* 3. Three – Susanna and twins called Judith and Hamnet 4. The Globe Theatre 5. Joseph Fiennes 6. *The Merry Wives of Windsor* 7. Anne Hathaway 8. Antonio 9. *The Taming Of The Shrew* 10. *Hamlet, Macbeth, King Lear* and *Othello*

The Life and Times of Muhammed Ali

Born Cassius Clay in 1942, Muhammed Ali is considered by many judges to be the greatest boxer of all time. To follow – a selection of pugilistic posers on the life of the Louisville Lip.

1. Who did Ali defeat to become the World Heavyweight Champion for the first time?
2. In 1996, Ali lit the Olympic flame at which American venue?
3. Who was the only British boxer to knock down Ali?
4. Which actor plays the title role in the 2001 film *Ali*?
5. At which weight did Muhammed Ali win an Olympic gold medal in 1960?
6. Ali starred as himself in the 1977 film, *The Greatest*. Which Hollywood actor played his trainer Angelo Dundee in the film?
7. What is the name of Ali's daughter who has followed her father into the boxing ring?
8. Ali memorably defeated George Foreman in the rumble in the jungle. In which country was the jungle?
9. Of his 61 professional fights how many did Ali lose?
10. In which war did he refuse to fight which resulted in him being stripped of his world title?

ANSWERS

1. Sonny Liston 2. Atlanta 3. Henry Cooper 4. Will Smith 5. Light heavyweight 6. Ernest Borgnine 7. Leila 8. Zaire 9. Five 10. Vietnam War

The Life and Times of Bugs Bunny

Bugs Bunny, the carrot-crunching cartoon character, first burst onto the screens in a 1940 short directed by Tex Avery. Below are ten rabbity riddles on one of the most enduring cartoon characters in cinema history.

1. Which film company first made the Bugs Bunny cartoons?
2. Who first voiced Bugs Bunny?
3. Which animator, a co-creator of Bugs Bunny and Roadrunner, died in February 2002 aged 89?
4. Which cigar-chomping film star is said to have provided the inspiration for Bugs Bunny?
5. Which catchphrase of Bugs Bunny was also the title of a 1972 film starring Barbra Streisand?
6. Which cartoon character often referred to Bugs as, 'a wascally wabbit'?
7. In which film did Bugs appear alongside basketball superstar Michael Jordan?
8. Which red-bearded hombre was continually outwitted by Bugs Bunny?
9. Which adversary of Bugs first appeared in a 1954 cartoon called *Devil May Hare*?
10. Bugs was first seen crunching a carrot in a 1940 cartoon. Was its title *The Easter Bunny*, *A Wild Hare* or *That Crazy Rabbit*?

ANSWERS
1. Warner Brothers 2. Mel Blanc 3. Chuck Jones 4. Groucho Marx 5. What's up, Doc? 6. Elmer J Fudd 7. *Space Jam* 8. Yosemite Sam 9. A Tasmanian Devil called Taz 10. *A Wild Hare*

The Life and Times of Julie Andrews

Julie Andrews was born Julia Wells in 1935 and her first starring role in the 1964 film _Mary Poppins_ earned her a Best Actress Oscar. The hills are alive with the sound of trivia on the life of Julie Andrews.

1. What is the first name of the character played by Julie Andrews in the film, _The Sound Of Music?_

2. In which Hitchcock thriller did she appear in 1966?

3. Name the film director famed for the Pink Panther films that Julie married?

4. In which stage production did Julie play the character of Eliza Doolittle?

5. What was the title of the 1982 film in which she played a transvestite?

6. What was the surname of the children who Mary Poppins looked after?

7. Whose life story was portrayed by Julie in the 1968 film _Star?_

8. In which film directed by her husband did Andrews co-star with Bo Derek and Dudley Moore?

9. In which 1981 film did Julie shock her legion of fans by appearing topless?

10. In the film, _The Sound Of Music_ which actress played the Mother Superior?

The Life and Times of Davy Crockett

Davy Crockett was born on August 17, 1786 and was one of the brave 189 defenders who perished at the Battle of the Alamo in 1836. Below is a selection of trivia teasers on the man known as The King of the Wild Frontier.

1. According to the song, 'The Ballad of Davy Crockett', he was born on a mountaintop. Is this true?
2. Davy Crockett's famous headgear was made from the hide of which wild animal?
3. In which state of the USA was Davy Crockett born?
4. Who directed and starred as Davy in the film, *The Alamo*?
5. Which of the following words does not appear on the tombstone of Davy Crockett? Pioneer, Patriot, Soldier, Hunter, Trapper, Explorer, State legislator, Congressman.
6. Which state was home to the Alamo where Davy died?
7. What name did Crockett give to his rifle?
8. Who, immortalised in the name of a knife, died alongside Davy at the Battle of the Alamo?
9. In 1816, Davy contracted a disease which almost killed him. Was it typhoid, smallpox or malaria?
10. According to the legend, Davy Crockett killed 105 what in a six-month period in 1825?

The Life and Times of David Bowie

In 1947, David Bowie was born David Robert Jones, which he changed to Bowie to avoid confusion with Davy Jones of the Monkees. Below is an album of questions and answers on the man known as the Thin White Duke.

1. Who co-wrote the song 'Fame' with David Bowie?
2. Who did Bowie play in the controversial film, *The Last Temptation of Christ*?
3. By what one-word name is Bowie's second wife known?
4. What is the name of the rock band that he formed in 1989?
5. In which 1986 fantasy film did he play the Goblin King?
6. Which song did Bowie release in 1969 to coincide with the Apollo 11 moon landing?
7. Who did David Bowie divorce in 1980?
8. In which touring stage play did Bowie play John Merrick?
9. Where was David Bowie dancing with Mick Jagger in a 1985 charity hit?
10. In 1983 what became the first Bowie single to top the charts in the UK and the USA?

ANSWERS
1. John Lennon 2. Pontius Pilate 3. Iman 4. Tin Machine 5. *Labyrinth* 6. 'Space Oddity' 7. Angie Bowie 8. *The Elephant Man* 9. In the street 10. 'Let's Dance'.

The Life and Times of John F Kennedy

When JFK was elected as the USA's 35th president in 1961 he became America's first Roman Catholic president.
Below are ten political posers on the life of JFK.

1. Who was arrested for the assassination of JFK but never stood trial?
2. What was the maiden name of his wife Jackie?
3. Who directed the 1991 film *JFK*?
4. What was the former name of New York's John F Kennedy Airport?
5. In what month and year was JFK assassinated?
6. Who was the vice-president of John F Kennedy?
7. Which brother of JFK was assassinated in 1968 by Sirhan Sirhan?
8. JFK was born May 29, 1917 in which US state?
9. Which actor played JFK in a 1983 TV mini series?
10. What does the F stand for in his name?

ANSWERS
1. Lee Harvey Oswald 2. Bouvier 3. Oliver Stone 4. Idlewild Airport 5. November 1963
6. Lyndon B Johnson 7. Robert Kennedy 8. Massachusetts 9. Martin Sheen
10. Fitzgerald

The Life and Times of Harry Potter

**J K Rowling created the literary wizard Harry Potter.
Warner Brothers have bought the rights to the films,
which see Daniel Radcliffe in the title role. Below are ten
magical mysteries on Harry Potter for you to unravel.**

1. What is the name of Harry's pet owl?

2. Harry owns a Nimbus 2000. What is a Nimbus 2000?

3. What is the name of the shop from which Harry purchased his wand?

4. What is the name of Harry Potter's bad-tempered uncle?

5. How many heads does Fluffy the dog have?

6. What name do the Hogwarts wizards give to non-wizards?

7. Who plays Hagrid in the Harry Potter films?

8. What is the last name of the twins, Fred and George?

9. What is the name of the bank where Harry Potter gets his money?

10. Which house do Harry and Ron belong to at Hogwarts?

ANSWERS
1. Hedwig 2. A high-quality broomstick 3. Olivanders 4. Uncle Vernon 5. Three
6. Muggles 7. Robbie Coltrane 8. Weasly 9. Grin Gots Bank 10. Griffindor

The Life and Times of **Al Capone**

Al Capone the Mafia leader was born in 1899 and died in 1947. Test your knowledge on the USA's most notorious criminal with the following montage of Mafia mindbenders.

1. What nickname was given to Al Capone due to an injury he sustained when he was 17?

2. In 1931 Capone received an 11-year jail sentence for what crime?

3. What is Al short for in the name of Al Capone?

4. Members of whose gang were brutally murdered in the St Valentine's Day Massacre?

5. In which 1987 film did Robert DeNiro play Al Capone?

6. What was the name of Al Capone's brother who was killed in a shoot-out with the police in 1924?

7. Al Capone's business card read 'Second-hand' what?

8. In 1925, which Mafia boss retired to leave Capone in charge of Chicago's South Side?

9. In which city was Al Capone born?

10. In what year did the St Valentine's Day Massacre take place?

ANSWERS
1. Scarface 2. Tax evasion 3. Alphonse 4. Bugsy Moran 5. *The Untouchables* 6. Frank Capone 7. Furniture dealer 8. Johnny Torrio 9. New York 10. 1929

The Life and Times of Elizabeth Taylor

Liz Taylor was born in 1932 and made her big-screen debut as a child star in the 1942 film, *There's One Born Every Minute*. Below are ten trivia teasers on the turbulent life of Liz Taylor.

1. Which screen canine was Liz Taylor's co-star in several films in the 1940s?

2. Who did she fall in love with on the film set of *Cleopatra*?

3. Which 1966 film earned Liz a Best Actress Oscar?

4. In which 1944 film did Liz Taylor compete in the Grand National?

5. In which 1994 film did she play the mother of Wilma Slaghoople?

6. What was the title of the 1980 film based on an Agatha Christie novel in which Taylor co-starred with Tony Curtis and Rock Hudson?

7. Who played her father in the 1950, comedy *Father Of The Bride*?

8. At which pop superstar's ranch did Liz Taylor marry Larry Fortensky?

9. What was the title of the 1958 film, based on a Tennessee Williams play, in which Liz co-starred with Paul Newman?

10. Who was the first husband of Elizabeth Taylor?

ANSWERS

1. Lassie 2. Richard Burton 3. Who's Afraid Of Virginia Woolf? 4. National Velvet 5. The Flintstones 6. The Mirror Crack'd 7. Spencer Tracy 8. Michael Jackson 9. Cat On A Hot Tin Roof 10. Michael Wilding

The Life and Times of Martina Navratilova

Tennis star Martina Navratilova was born in 1956 and in her career won a total of 167 singles titles including 18 Grand Slam singles titles. Below is a volley of ten tennis teasers on the life of Martina.

1. In which European capital city was Martina born?

2. Nicknamed Little Miss Poker Face, who was Martina's great rival during the 1970s and 80s?

3. From 1983 to 1985 Martina won 109 consecutive women's doubles matches. Who was her partner?

4. How many Wimbledon singles titles did Martina win?

5. In what year did Martina retire from playing professional singles matches?

6. In 1991 which gay former lover of Martina sued her for palimony?

7. Did Martina become a US citizen in 1981, 1983 or 1985?

8. In which tennis cup competition did Martina lead Czechoslovakia to victory in 1975?

9. Martina now lives in the ski resort of Aspen in which American state?

10. Which Grand Slam singles tournament did Martina win the least number of times?

ANSWERS
1. Prague 2. Chris Evert Lloyd 3. Pam Shriver 4. Nine 5. 1994 6. Judy Nelson 7. 1981 8. Federation Cup 9. Colorado 10. French Open, which she won twice

The Life and Times of the Bronte Sisters

The Brontë sisters Anne, Emily and Charlotte were three of six children born to Anglican clergyman Patrick Brontë. Test your literary logic with the questions below on the life of the Brontës.

1. What was the only published novel of Emily Brontë?
2. Which novel by Anne Brontë opens in the autumn of 1827?
3. Which village in West Yorkshire was the home of the Brontës from 1820?
4. In 1846, what title was given to the collection of poems written by the sisters?
5. In which European capital city is the Charlotte Brontë novel, *Villette*, set?
6. What was the name of the Brontë sisters' brother who died in 1848?
7. Which disease killed Emily Brontë?
8. What is the surname of the central family in the novel, *Wuthering Heights*?
9. Who was the youngest of the Brontë sisters?
10. What was the title of Charlotte Brontë's first novel, originally rejected by publishers but eventually published posthumously in 1857?

ANSWERS
1. *Wuthering Heights* 2. *The Tenant of Wildfell Hall* 3. Haworth 4. *Poems by Currer, Ellis and Acton Bell* 5. Brussels 6. Branwell 7. TB or consumption 8. Earnshaw 9. Anne 10. *The Professor*

The Life and Times of Whitney Houston

Whitney Houston was born in New Jersey in 1963 and early in her career sang backing vocals for Chaka Khan. Below is a soulful selection of questions on the life of Whitney Houston.

1. Who wrote the Whitney hit 'I Will Always Love You'?
2. Which patriotic song did Whitney sing at Superbowl XXV in 1991?
3. Which former member of the boy band New Edition did Whitney marry?
4. In which film did Whitney play a singer called Rachel Marron?
5. Which song released by Whitney in 1988 was used as a theme for the LA Olympics?
6. What is the name of Whitney Houston's gospel-singer mother?
7. What was the first single by Whitney Houston to top the charts in the UK and the USA?
8. In 1988, Whitney headlined the 70th birthday party concert of which African politician?
9. The 1998 hit 'When You Believe' featured Whitney performing a duet with which other high-profile female singer?
10. What was the title of the 1995 film in which she co-starred with Angela Bassett and Gregory Hines?

The Life and Times of Joan of Arc

Born in 1412 Joan of Arc died whilst attempting to help Charles VII reclaim the throne of France. Below are ten questions on the life of this French national heroine.

1. Joan of Arc was also referred to as the Maid of where?

2. In which war did Joan of Arc battle against the English?

3. In which century was Joan of Arc canonised?

4. With what first name was Joan of Arc christened?

5. In which town was she burnt at the stake?

6. Who played the title role in the 1948 film, *Joan of Arc*?

7. How old was Joan when she was executed?

8. What was the name of the poor peasant father of Joan of Arc?

9. Which Irish writer penned the play, *St Joan*?

10. What is the name of the French village where Joan was born?

The Life and Times of Batman

Batman began life as a comic-strip character and was later adapted into a TV series, several films and a number of cartoon series. To follow are ten teasers on the super-hero known as the Caped Crusader.

1. What is the secret identity of Batman?

2. By what name is Batman's foe Selina Kyle also known?

3. What is the name of the Police Commissioner of Gotham City?

4. Which of Batman's enemies wore a green costume decorated with question marks?

5. In which comics did Batman first appear?

6. Who played the Caped Crusader in the 1989 film, *Batman*?

7. Who created the character of Batman?

8. Which actor played Batman in the 1960s TV series?

9. How were Robin's parents killed?

10. Which actress played Dr Chase Meridian in the 1995 film, *Batman Forever*?

ANSWERS
1. Bruce Wayne 2. Catwoman 3. Commissioner Gordon 4. The Riddler 5. DC, which stood for Detective Comics 6. Michael Keaton 7. Bob Kane 8. Adam West 9. In an accident in a circus high-wire act 10. Nicole Kidman

The Life and Times of James Bond

James Bond first burst onto the big screen in the 1962 film, *Dr No* and in 2002 the Bond films received a special BAFTA Award. Below is a selection of ten questions that are licensed to thrill.

1. Which actress played the first Bond girl, Honey Ryder?
2. What was the first James Bond novel?
3. Which character has been played on film by Lois Maxwell and Samantha Bond?
4. The 1990 film, *Spymaker* was about the life of who?
5. In which film did Grace Jones play the character of Mayday?
6. In which film did Pierce Brosnan make his debut as 007?
7. Who made his only appearance as Bond in the film, *On Her Majesty's Secret Service*?
8. Which US building did the Bond villain Goldfinger plan to break into?
9. Which cocktail does Bond always have served shaken not stirred?
10. Hugo Drax was the adversary of 007 in which film?

ANSWERS

1. Ursula Andress 2. *Casino Royale* 3. Miss Moneypenny 4. Ian Fleming 5. *A View To A Kill* 6. *Goldeneye* 7. George Lazenby 8. Fort Knox 9. Vodka martini 10. *Moonraker*

The Life and Times of Vincent Van Gogh

Vincent Van Gogh was born in 1853 in a village called Zundent and committed suicide in 1890. Below is a selection of ten artistic questions and answers on the life of Van Gogh.

1. How many paintings did Van Gogh sell in his lifetime?
2. Which city houses the Vincent Van Gogh Museum?
3. Which painting, his first large-scale composition and first masterpiece, did Van Gogh paint in 1885?
4. In 1972, who recorded a hit record entitled 'Vincent'?
5. Which of his ears did Van Gogh cut off?
6. Which painting by Van Gogh sold for £22.5 million in a 1987 auction at Christie's in London?
7. In 1881, Vincent fell in love with Kee Vos-Stricker. What relation was she to Van Gogh?
8. In which film did Kirk Douglas play Van Gogh and Anthony Quinn play Paul Gaugin?
9. How did Van Gogh kill himself?
10. What was the middle name of Vincent Van Gogh?

ANSWERS
1.One 2.Amsterdam 3. *The Potato Eaters* 4. Don McLean 5. Left ear 6. *Sunflowers* 7. His cousin 8. *Lust For Life* 9. Shot himself in the chest 10.Willem

SESSION 3

The Life and Times of Charles Dickens

Charles Dickens was born in 1812 and died in 1870 leaving a legacy of classic novels. Do you have great expectations of scoring ten out of ten on the following Dickensian dilemmas?

1. Sydney Carton and Charles Darnay are the central characters in which novel?

2. Which Dickens character has an uncle called Ralph, a friend called Smike and a wife called Madeline?

3. Which novel was Dickens writing at the time of his death?

4. Betsy Trotwood is the aunt of which Dickens character?

5. What is the name of the escaped convict in the novel, *Great Expectations*?

6. The title of which Dickens novel was named after the home of the novel's central character John Jarndyce?

7. In *Pickwick Papers*, what is the first name of Mr Pickwick, the founder of the Pickwick Club?

8. What is the title of the 1988 Disney cartoon film based on the story of Oliver Twist?

9. Which novel ends with the line, 'God bless us everyone'?

10. Which Dickens novel features a peg-legged villain called Silas Wegg?

The Life and Times of Diana Ross

Diana Ross was born in Detroit in 1944 and after leaving the Supremes in 1970 she had her first of many solo hits with the song 'Reach Out And Touch (Somebody's Hand)'. Below are ten supreme sound bites on the life of Diana Ross.

1. To which record label did the Supremes sign in 1960?

2. In which 1978 film did Diana Ross co-star with Michael Jackson and Richard Pryor?

3. When Diana left the Supremes in 1970, who replaced her?

4. Who did she duet with when singing the theme for the 1981 film, *Endless Love*?

5. Which 1982 hit for Diana Ross was written by Michael Jackson?

6. What was the original name of the Supremes?

7. Who did Diana Ross portray in the 1972 film, *Lady Sings The Blues*?

8. Which trio wrote the Diana Ross hit, 'Chain Reaction'?

9. The song, 'Do You Know Where You're Going To', was the theme for which 1975 film?

10. Which soul legend collaborated with Diana on the hit record, 'You Are Everything'?

ANSWERS
1. Motown 2. *The Wiz* 3. Jean Terrell 4. Lionel Richie 5. 'Muscles' 6. The Primettes 7. Billie Holliday 8. The Bee Gees 9. *Mahogany* 10. Marvin Gaye

The Life and Times of Henry VIII

Henry VIII was born in 1491, ascended to the throne in 1509 and was famed for having six wives. Below are ten regal riddles on the life of Henry VIII.

1. What first name was shared by three of Henry VIII's wives?

2. Who played Henry in the film, *Anne Of A Thousand Days*?

3. Who was the only queen to bear Henry VIII a son?

4. Who was executed for treason on the orders of Henry VIII on July 6, 1535?

5. Did Henry VIII have three wives in 1532, 1534 or 1536?

6. Which royal house did Henry VIII belong to?

7. In which decade did Henry VIII die?

8. What name was given to the venue of the jousting tournament of 1520 where Henry met Francis I of France to arrange an alliance?

9. Who was the last wife of Henry VIII?

10. Who succeeded Henry VIII to the throne?

The Life and Times of Adolph Hitler

Adolph Hitler was born in Austria in 1899 and in 1921 became leader of the Nazi Party.
Below are ten questions on the life of the dictator known as Der Fuhrer.

1. Which organisation for teenage German boys was founded by Hitler in 1926?

2. In what year did Hitler become the chancellor of Germany?

3. What was the name of the political party that Hitler joined in 1919?

4. What surname was Hitler born with?

5. For what crime was Hitler imprisoned in 1924?

6. Whilst serving his prison sentence he dictated his book, *Mein Kampf* to his secretary, Rudolph Hess. How does its title translate into English?

7. Which mystical symbol did Hitler choose to represent the Nazis on their flag?

8. In which World War I battle was Hitler wounded in the leg by a shell fragment?

9. What was the name of Hitler's secret state police, founded in 1933?

10. What was officially opened by Hitler on August 1, 1936?

ANSWERS
1.The Hitler Youth 2. 1933 3.The German Workers' Party 4. Schicklgruber 5. Treason 6. My Struggle 7. Swastika 8. Battle of the Somme 9. Gestapo, shortened from Geheime Staats Polizei 10.The Berlin Olympics

3

The Life and Times of Steven Spielberg

Stevhen Spielberg was born December 18, 1947. From the humble beginnings of directing made-for-TV movies he graduated to become the world's most successful film director. Below is a medley of movie questions on the life of Steven Spielberg.

1. Which 1977 film climaxed with Richard Dreyfuss stepping into an alien spacecraft?
2. Who played Captain Quint in the film, *Jaws*?
3. In the 2001 film, *AI*, Haley Joel Osment plays a unique robot boy. What do the initials *AI* stand for?
4. Name Spielberg's second wife, who he met at the auditions for the film, *Indiana Jones and the Temple of Doom*.
5. Captain John Miller was the lead character in which 1999 film?
6. Which film directed by Spielberg and starring Whoopi Goldberg did not win a single Oscar despite being nominated in eleven categories?
7. Which film earned Spielberg his first Oscar for Best Director?
8. Which Hollywood movie studio was founded in 1994 by Spielberg?
9. Who played the sister of Elliot in the film *ET*?
10. Which Spielberg film starring John Malkovich was based on an autobiographical novel by J G Ballard?

The Life and Times of Jack Nicklaus

Jack Nicklaus was born in Ohio in 1940 and went on to become the most successful golfer in the history of the sport. Below is a round of golf questions on the life of Jack Nicklaus.

1. Did Jack contest his first pro tournament in 1960, 1961 or 1962?

2. Which animal provides Jack's nickname?

3. Which Major did Jack Nicklaus win in 1966, 1970 and 1978?

4. How old was Nicklaus when he won his first Major competition, the Ohio Open?

5. Jack married in 1960. Is his wife called Barbara, Beverly or Belinda?

6. The Jack Nicklaus Museum opened in his hometown in 2002. In which town is the museum?

7. During the 1960s Nicklaus, Arnold Palmer and which other golfer were known as the Big Three?

8. What is the name of the son of Jack Nicklaus who has followed in his father's footsteps to become a professional golfer?

9. Which of the Majors did Jack win in 1986 at the age of 46?

10. How many Majors did Jack win in his career, was it 16, 18 or 20?

The Life and Times of Agatha Christie

Agatha Christie was born Agatha May Clarissa Miller in the English county of Devon in 1890. She became one of the world's most translated writers and was made a Dame in 1971. Below are ten mysteries on the lady known as the Queen of Crime.

1. According to the title of a 1957 book by Christie what time was the train from Paddington?

2. Which 1934 novel had the alternative title of *Murder On The Calais Coach*?

3. What was the first name of Miss Marple?

4. Agatha's first published novel, *The Mysterious Affair At Styles*, introduced which detective?

5. Who played Christie in the 1979 film, *Agatha*?

6. Which archaeologist became the second husband of Agatha in 1930?

7. Which play written by Agatha opened in London in 1952 and became the continuously longest-running play in theatrical history?

8. Was Agatha 76, 86 or 96 when she died?

9. Who played Miss Marple in the 1961 film, *Murder She Said*?

10. Under what pseudonym did Agatha write six romantic novels?

The Life and Times of the Rolling Stones

The Rolling Stones were formed in 1962 and have had chart-topping singles on both sides of the Atlantic, including 'Paint It Black' and 'Honky Tonk Woman'. Below are ten rocking riddles on the bad boys of pop.

1. Which model was Bill Wyman married to for 17 months?

2. Which Australian outlaw was played by Mick Jagger in a 1969 film?

3. What is the name of the drummer for the Stones?

4. Which college was attended by Mick Jagger and John F Kennedy?

5. Which member of the Stones was found dead in his swimming pool in 1969?

6. The Rolling Stones took their name from a song by which blues musician?

7. Born on October 21, 1971, what is the name of Mick Jagger's daughter?

8. Which pop artist designed the sleeve for the Rolling Stones album, *Sticky Fingers*?

9. Which member of the Stones served in the RAF?

10. Which song contains the line, 'It's a gas gas gas'?

ANSWERS
1. Mandy Smith 2. Ned Kelly 3. Charlie Watts 4. The London School of Economics 5. Brian Jones 6. Muddy Waters 7. Jade 8. Andy Warhol 9. Bill Wyman 10. 'Jumpin' Jack Flash'.

3

The Life and Times of Julius Caesar

Julius Caesar, the last dictator of Rome, was assassinated on
the Ides of March by a group of Roman senators.
Below are ten Roman riddles on the life and death of
Julius Caesar.

1. In 49BC which river did Caesar's troops cross to begin a civil war?

2. According to William Shakespeare what were Caesar's last three words?

3. Who was Caesar's second-in-command at the time of his assassination?

4. Who played Julius in the comedy film, *Carry On Cleo*?

5. Who did Caesar marry after Pompeia?

6. In what year did Caesar die?

7. What was Quinctilis renamed in memory of Caesar?

8. Which actor played Caesar in the 1963 film, *Cleopatra*?

9. Which of the conspirators is said to have struck the first blow in the assassination of Caesar?

10. Caesar's motto as he conquered new provinces for Rome was, 'Veni, vidi, vici.' How does this translate into English?

ANSWERS
1.The Rubicon 2.'Et tu Brute' 3. Marc Antony 4. Kenneth Williams 5. Calpurnia
6. 44BC 7.The month of July, which was originally called Quinctilis, and was renamed after
Caesar, who was born on July 13 8. Rex Harrison 9. Casca 10.'I came, I saw, I
conquered'.

34

The Life and Times of Sherlock Holmes

The literary detective Sherlock Holmes first appeared in a serial in *Strand* magazine and went on to become the most portrayed literary character on film. Below are ten elementary equations for you to solve.

1. Who created the character of Sherlock Holmes?
2. What was the title of the story in which Sherlock Holmes made his literary debut?
3. Who played Sherlock Holmes on film when Dudley Moore played Dr Watson?
4. What is the name of Sherlock's Baker Street landlady?
5. Which drug was Sherlock addicted to?
6. Which novel contains chapters called 'Three Broken Threads' and 'Death On The Moor'?
7. What is the first name of Dr Watson?
8. What is the name of the waterfalls at which Sherlock Holmes fell to his death?
9. Which actor born in 1892 played Sherlock the greatest number of times on film?
10. What is the number of Sherlock's house on Baker Street?

ANSWERS
1. Arthur Conan Doyle 2. *A Study In Scarlet* 3. Peter Cooke 4. Mrs Hudson 5. Cocaine 6. *The Hound Of The Baskervilles* 7. John 8. Reichenbach Falls 9. Basil Rathbone 10. 221b

The Life and Times of Robin Williams

Robin Williams was born in Chicago in 1952. His show business career began as a stand-up comedian before he got his big break playing a zany alien in the sitcom *Mork & Mindy*. Below is a selection of trivia teasers on the life of Robin Williams.

1. Which 1980 film saw Robin smoking a pipe and chewing spinach?
2. In which 1987 film did Robin play a disc jockey in the armed forces?
3. In which box office hit of 1993 did Robin play Daniel Hillard and a Scottish nanny?
4. Who played Mindy in *Mork & Mindy*?
5. In which 1990 film did Robin play Dr Malcolm Sayer?
6. What was the title of the 1997 film that earned Robin an Oscar for Best Supporting Actor?
7. In which 1996 film did he play a gay Miami nightclub owner?
8. Who did Mork talk to at the end of every episode of *Mork & Mindy*?
9. Which Shakespearian character did he play in the 1996 version of *Hamlet*?
10. In which 1989 box office flop did Robin play the King of the Moon?

ANSWERS
1. *Popeye* 2. *Good Morning Vietnam* 3. *Mrs Doubtfire* 4. Pam Dawber 5. *Awakenings* 6. *Good Will Hunting* 7. *The Birdcage* 8. Orson 9. Osric 10. *The Adventures of Baron Munchausen*

The Life and Times of the Rat Pack

Frank Sinatra, Dean Martin, Sammy Davis Jnr, Peter Lawford and Joey Bishop were collectively known as the Rat Pack. Below are ten questions on this ensemble of entertainment legends.

1. The Frank Sinatra song, 'Three Coins In A Fountain' referred to which fountain?

2. Dean Martin made 16 films with which comedy actor?

3. Which actress was referred to as the Rat Pack's Girl Friday?

4. Which member of the Rat Pack was the brother-in-law of John F Kennedy?

5. The Pack made the Copa Room at the Sands Hotel their home. In which city is the Sands Hotel?

6. What is the middle name of Frank Sinatra?

7. Which comedy film and sequel saw Sammy Davis Jnr and Dean Martin posing as priests?

8. Which film did the Rat Pack make together that was remade in the 21st century with George Clooney, Brad Pitt and Elliot Gould?

9. Which member of the Rat Pack died in 1990?

10. For which 1954 film did Sinatra win an Oscar for Best Supporting Actor?

ANSWERS

1. Trevi Fountain 2. Jerry Lewis 3. Shirley Maclaine 4. Peter Lawford 5. Las Vegas 6. Albert 7. Cannonball Run 8. Oceans Eleven 9. Sammy Davis Jnr 10. From Here To Eternity

The Life and Times of Stephen King

Stephen King, the world's leading horror novelist, was born in September 1947 in the town of Portland. Below are ten terrifying teasers on the master of the macabre.

1. Which 1983 novel by King told the story of a haunted car?

2. Under what pen name did he write the story, *The Running Man*?

3. Which King novel featured a rabid St Bernard dog?

4. Which 1986 film starring River Phoenix was based on a Stephen King short story entitled *The Body*?

5. Published in 1974, what is the title of King's first novel that was adapted into a 1976 film directed by Brian de Palma?

6. Which novel is set in a haunted hotel called the Overlook?

7. Which actor played on film Paul Sheldon, the author of the Misery novels?

8. In which state was Stephen King born?

9. Who did King collaborate with for the novel, *The Talisman*?

10. What type of establishment is Shawshank in the story and film, *The Shawshank Redemption*?

The Life and Times of the Osmonds

The Osmonds made their television debut on the Andy Williams Show and went on to become teenybopper pop idols in the 1970s. Below are ten trivia teasers on the life of the Osmonds.

1. What religion is adhered to by the Osmond family?

2. Who wrote the song, 'Puppy Love' a hit for Donny Osmond?

3. Which member of the Osmonds had a hit with the song, 'Paper Roses'?

4. Which song, a hit for Donny in 1973, was originally recorded by Nat King Cole?

5. Who is the oldest of the Osmond brothers?

6. Which song by the Osmonds was concerned with the polluting effects of the motorcar?

7. In which stage musical did Donny sing, 'Any Dream Will Do'?

8. What was the title of the first hit single for the Osmond brothers?

9. Which Osmond hit of the 1970s was covered by Boyzone in the 1990s?

10. In which state was Donny Osmond born?

ANSWERS
1. Mormon 2. Paul Anka 3. Marie Osmond 4. 'When I Fall In Love' 5. Alan 6. 'Crazy Horses' 7. *Joseph And The Technicolor Dreamcoat* 8. 'One Bad Apple' 9. 'Love Me For A Reason' 10. Utah

The Life and Times of Abraham Lincoln

Abraham Lincoln was born in the state of Kentucky in 1809 and was elected president of the USA in 1861. Below are ten political posers on the life of Abe Lincoln.

1. Was Lincoln the 15th, 16th or 17th president of the USA?
2. Who did Lincoln marry on November 4, 1842?
3. What name is given to the speech made by Lincoln on November 19, 1863?
4. On which mountain can a carving of Lincoln's head be seen alongside those of George Washington, Thomas Jefferson and Theodore Roosevelt?
5. Who assassinated Abraham Lincoln?
6. What was the title of the play that Lincoln was watching when the fatal shot that led to his death was fired?
7. Which future president did Lincoln appoint as general-in-chief of the Federal Armies in 1864?
8. Which party nominated Lincoln for the US Senate in 1858?
9. Which film star from a famous acting family portrayed Abe in the 1939 film, *Young Mr Lincoln*?
10. On May 4, 1865 Abraham Lincoln was laid to rest at the Oak Ridge Cemetery. In which US state is the cemetery?

ANSWERS
1. 16th President 2. Mary Todd 3. The Gettysburg Address 4. Mount Rushmore 5. John Wilkes Booth 6. *Our American Cousin* 7. Ulysses S Grant 8. Republican Party 9. Henry Fonda 10. Illinois

The Life and Times of the Simpsons

The dysfunctional cartoon family, the Simpsons, was created by Matt Groening and over took the Flintstones as the longest-running cartoon family on TV.
Below are ten questions on the animated antics of the residents of Springfield.

1. On whose TV show did the Simpsons make their television debut?

2. What is the name of the bar where Homer drinks his Duff beer?

3. What vehicle does Otto Man drive in Springfield?

4. What is the name of the aide of Mr Burns?

5. What job is held by Julius Hibert in Springfield?

6. What is the name of the convenience-store clerk in *The Simpsons*?

7. Nancy Cartwright provides the voice of which member of the Simpson family?

8. What is the name of Krusty the Clown's evil assistant and arch-enemy of Bart?

9. What musical instrument is played by Lisa Simpson?

10. What was the maiden name of Marge Simpson?

ANSWERS
1. Tracy Ullman 2. Moe's Tavern 3. The school bus 4. Waylon Smithers 5. Doctor 6. Apu 7. Bart Simpson 8. Sideshow Bob 9. Saxophone 10. Bouvier

The Life and Times of Jack Nicholson

Jack Nicholson was born on April 22, 1937 and received the first of several Oscar nominations for the 1969 film *Easy Rider*. Below are ten trivia titbits on the life of Jack Nicholson.

1. In which 1992 drama did Jack play Colonel Nathan Jessup and Tom Cruise play Lieutenant Daniel Kaffe?

2. For which 1997 comedy, in which he falls in love with Helen Hunt, did Nicholson receive a Best Actor Oscar?

3. Cher, Susan Sarandon and Michelle Pfeiffer were Nicholson's co-stars in which 1987 film?

4. What is the title of the 1996 film in which Jack plays President Dale?

5. The 1990 film, *The Two Jakes* was a belated sequel to which 1974 film?

6. What was the title of the film based on a novel by Ken Kesey, which was set in a mental institution?

7. In which 1983 film did Nicholson play a retired astronaut?

8. Jack Nicholson played a character called Jack Napier in which 1989 film?

9. In 1968 Jack wrote the screenplay for a film entitled *Head*. The film told the story of which pop group?

10. Which Teamster Union leader did Nicholson play in a 1992 film directed by Danny Devito?

ANSWERS

1. A Few Good Men 2. As Good As It Gets 3. The Witches Of Eastwick 4. Mars Attacks 5. Chinatown 6. One Flew Over The Cuckoo's Nest 7. Terms Of Endearment 8. Batman – Jack Napier became The Joker 9. The Monkees 10. Jimmy Hoffa in a film entitled Hoffa

The Life and Times of Michael Schumacher

Michael Schumacher was born in the German town of Hurth-Hermulheim and made his Formula One debut in 1991. Below are ten racy riddles on the man that many judges consider to be the greatest-ever driver in the history of Formula One.

1. Michael Schumacher won the opening Grand Prix race of 2002 in March. Which country staged the race?

2. In what year did Michael first become Formula One World Champion?

3. Which racing team did he join in 1996?

4. What is the name of Michael's brother, who is also a Formula One driver?

5. In 1987 Schumacher was crowned German and European Champion in which sport?

6. Was Michael Schumacher born in 1968, 1969 Or 1970?

7. With which racing team did Michael make his Formula One Grand Prix debut?

8. In 1992 Schumacher won his first-ever Grand Prix race in which European country?

9. In 1998 Michael finished second to which driver in the Formula One World Championships?

10. For which racing team did Michael secure his first Grand Prix point?

ANSWERS

1. Australia 2. 1994 3. Ferrari 4. Ralf 5. Karting 6. 1969 7. Jordan 8. Belgium 9. Mika Hakkinen 10. Benetton

The Life and Times of Dracula

The novel *Dracula* was published in 1897 and a medieval ruler of Wallachia, called Vlad the Impaler, inspired the character. Below is a barrage of blood-curdling questions on Count Dracula.

1. Who created the literary character of Count Dracula?

2. Who played Dracula in a 1992 film directed by Francis Ford Coppola?

3. Transylvania, the home of Dracula, is a region in which European country?

4. Which doctor, played many times on film by Peter Cushing, is the chief adversary of Dracula?

5. In the novel, at which Yorkshire town did Dracula come ashore from the ship *Demeter*?

6. What does the name of Dracula actually mean?

7. Which member of the onion family is repellent to vampires?

8. Name the actor famous for playing Dracula who died in 1956 and was buried in a black cape.

9. Who played the Count in the spoof horror movie, *Love At First Bite*?

10. For which British film company did Christopher Lee make numerous films playing Dracula?

ANSWERS
1. Bram Stoker. 2. Gary Oldman 3. Romania 4. Van Helsing 5. Whitby 6. Son of the Dragon 7. Garlic 8. Bela Lugosi 9. George Hamilton 10. Hammer Films

The Life and Times of Rod Stewart

Rod Stewart was born in London on January 10, 1945 and before making his name as a pop star was an apprentice footballer for Brentford Rovers. Below are ten rhythmic riddles on the life of Rod Stewart.

1. With which Swedish actress did Rod embark on a highly publicised love affair in 1975?

2. What instrument did Rod play on the 1960s hit, 'My Boy Lollipop' recorded by Millie?

3. What is Rod short for in the name to Rod Stewart?

4. Which group did Rod Stewart front on the 1971 hit, 'Stay With Me'?

5. What stretch of water did Rod cross according to the title of a 1975 album?

6. Which Beatles hit was covered by Rod Stewart in 1976?

7. With which nation's football World Cup squad did Rod record the song, 'Ole Ola'?

8. In 1990, Rod collaborated with which female artist on the song, 'It Takes Two'?

9. Who did Rod Stewart marry in 1979?

10. Which Rod Stewart hit contains the line, 'It's late September and I really should be back at school'?

ANSWERS
1. Britt Ekland 2. Harmonica 3. Roderick 4. The Faces 5. Atlantic – the album was entitled *Atlantic Crossing* 6. 'Get Back' 7. Scotland 8. Tina Turner 9. Alana Hamilton 10. 'Maggie May'.

SESSION 5

The Life and Times of Christopher Columbus

Christopher Columbus was born in 1451 and first went to sea in his teens before discovering America on a historic voyage. Below are ten questions exploring the life of Christopher Columbus.

1. On August 3, 1492, Columbus departed from Spain with three ships – the *Santa Maria*, the *Pinta* and which other ship?

2. The *Santa Maria* was shipwrecked in the Christmas of 1492 off the coast of which modern-day island?

3. What was the objective of his voyage of 1492?

4. Which French actor played Columbus in the 1992 film entitled *1492*?

5. Which king and queen of Spain financed the voyages of Columbus?

6. Did Columbus die in 1506, 1508 or 1510?

7. In which Italian city was Columbus born?

8. In 1498, on his third voyage to the New Worl,d which island did Columbus name after the Holy Trinity?

9. Who played Columbus in the film, *Carry On Columbus*?

10. In 1526, Diego, the eldest son of Columbus, was buried next to his father in which Spanish city?

ANSWERS

1. The *Nina* 2. Haiti 3. To find a new route to Asia. He believed that the Earth was smaller than it is and he would find a quicker route to the Far East enabling him to return with rich cargoes of silks and spices. 4. Gérard Depardieu 5. King Ferdinand and Queen Isabella 6. 1506 7. Genoa 8. Trinidad 9. Jim Dale 10. Seville

The Life and Times of Tarzan

The novel *Tarzan of the Apes* was published in 1912 and has inspired many films in which the apeman was played by a variety of actors, most notably Johnny Weismuller. **Below are ten teasers on Tarzan.**

1. How many films did Johnny Weismuller make as Tarzan?

2. Which Chicago-born author created the character of Tarzan?

3. Tarzan was first played on film in 1917 by which actor?

4. Who played the role of Tarzan in the 1960s TV series?

5. How many Olympic swimming gold medals did Johnny Weismuller win?

6. When Bo Derek played Jane who played Tarzan?

7. What does the name Tarzan mean?

8. Who replaced Johnny Weismuller in the role of Tarzan in the 1949 film, *Tarzan's Magic Fountain*?

9. Which actress provided the voice of the ape Kala in Disney's animated version of Tarzan?

10. What is the last name of Tarzan's female companion Jane?

ANSWERS

1. 12 2. Edgar Rice Burroughs 3. Elmo Lincoln 4. Ron Ely 5. Five in total, three in the 1924 games and a further two in 1928 6. Miles O'Keefe 7. White skin 8. Lex Barker 9. Glenn Close 10. Porter.

The Life and Times of Tom Cruise

Tom Cruise was born Thomas Mapother IV in 1962 and made his big-screen debut opposite Brooke Shields in the 1981 weepie, *Endless Love*. Below are ten questions on the life of one of Hollywood's biggest stars.

1. In which film based on a John Grisham novel did Cruise play a Mafia lawyer?

2. In which 1996 film did he first play the all-action hero Ethan Hawke?

3. What was the title of the 1988 film that saw Tom mixing Harvey Wallbangers and Pina Coladas?

4. In which film co-starring Cruise and Nicole Kidman did Tom play a stock-car racing-driver?

5. Which actor asked Tom to 'Show me the money', in the film *Jerry Maguire*?

6. Who played the autistic brother in the film *Rain Man*?

7. What was the call sign of the pilot played by Cruise in the film *Top Gun*?

8. Which actress did Tom Cruise marry in 1987 and divorce in 1990?

9. The 1999 film, *Eyes Wide Shut* starring Tom and Nicole Kidman, was the last film of which director?

10. In which film did Cruise receive an Oscar nomination for his portrayal of Ron Kovick, a paraplegic war veteran?

ANSWERS

1. The Firm 2. Mission Impossible 3. Cocktail 4. Days Of Thunder 5. Cuba Gooding Jnr 6. Dustin Hoffman 7. Maverick 8. Mimi Rogers 9. Stanley Kubrick 10. Born On The Fourth Of July

The Life and Times of Robin Hood

The legendary tales and adventures of Robin Hood have been recounted for over 600 years, and his heroic deeds have provided the inspiration for numerous film productions. Below is a selection of swashbuckling posers on the legend of Robin Hood.

1. What kind of animal did Disney use to portray Robin Hood in their animated film version?
2. Which right-hand man of Robin is renowned for his size and strength?
3. When Kevin Costner played Robin Hood on film who played Maid Marian?
4. What is the name of the tyrannical prince, a sworn enemy of Robin?
5. In which English county is Sherwood Forest, the hideout of Robin Hood and his Merry Men?
6. Which man of the cloth did Robin reputedly fight at Fountain Dale before inviting him to join his band of outlaws?
7. What is the name of Robin Hood's minstrel?
8. Who was known as the Robin Hood of Texas?
9. Who played the title role in the 1938 film, *The Adventures of Robin Hood*?
10. Who played the title role in the 1950s TV series, *The Adventures Of Robin Hood*?

ANSWERS
1. A fox 2. Little John 3. Mary Elizabeth Mastrantonio 4. Prince John 5. Nottinghamshire 6. Friar Tuck 7. Allan A Dale 8. Sam Bass 9. Errol Flynn 10. Richard Greene

The Life and Times of George Orwell

George Orwell was born in 1903 and died in 1950 leaving a legacy of literary classics. Below are ten questions on several chapters of Orwell's life and works.

1. In which Asian country was Orwell born?

2. What was the real name of George Orwell?

3. What two cities are mentioned in an Orwell book, published in 1933, that tells of his life as a vagrant?

4. What name is given to Britain in the novel *1984*?

5. What kind of animal is Napoleon in the Orwell novel, *Animal Farm*?

6. Where was the road leading to, according to the title of a book published by Orwell in 1937?

7. The 1938 novel *Homage To Catalonia* tells of Orwell's experiences in which country?

8. Set in Asia, what is the title of Orwell's first novel?

9. What name did Orwell give to the truth-denying language of Big Brother's rule in the novel *1984*?

10. What is the name of the farm in *Animal Farm*?

ANSWERS

1. India 2. Eric Arthur Blair 3. Paris and London – the novel was *Down And Out In Paris And London* 4. Airstrip One 5. A pig 6. Wigan Pier – the novel was *The Road To Wigan Pier* 7. Spain 8. *Burmese Days* 9. Newspeak 10. Manor Farm

The Life and Times of Madonna

Madonna was born in Michigan in 1958 and went on to become the most successful solo female artist in the history of pop music. Below is a musical montage of questions on the life of the Queen of Pop.

1. Who directed Madonna in the film *Evita*?

2. What is Madonna's middle name?

3. The lyrics of which Madonna hit mention a host of stars including Greta Garbo, Fred Astaire, Ginger Rogers, Jimmy Dean and Grace Kelly?

4. The Oscar-winning song, *Sooner Or Later*, was sung by Madonna in which film?

5. Which actor appeared as Austin Powers alongside Madonna in the video for the song 'Beautiful Stranger'?

6. Which actor did Madonna marry in 1985?

7. What was the title of the 1987 film in which Madonna starred alongside Sir John Mills?

8. Which song, originally a hit in 1972 for Don McLean, was covered by Madonna?

9. Which Madonna song opens with the line, 'Some boys kiss me, some boys hug me, I think they're OK'?

10. What was the title of the 1986 Madonna album that topped the charts on both sides of the Atlantic?

ANSWERS

1. Alan Parker 2. Louise 3. 'Vogue' 4. *Dick Tracy* 5. Mike Myers 6. Sean Penn 7. *Who's That Girl?* 8. 'American Pie' 9. 'Material Girl' 10. *True Blue*

The Life and Times of Napoleon Bonaparte

Napoleon Bonaparte was born on August 15, 1769 and rose from obscurity to become emperor of France. Below are ten questions on the leader known as the Man of Destiny.

1. On which Mediterranean island was Napoleon born?

2. What word completes the following saying attributed to Napoleon, 'An army marches on its ...'?

3. In 1793, Napoleon was promoted to general after the successful siege of which city?

4. In which battle was Napoleon defeated on June 18, 1815?

5. Napoleon Bonaparte was said to have described England as a nation of what?

6. What surname was Napoleon born with?

7. Who did he marry in 1796?

8. Which Hollywood superstar played Napoleon in the 1954 film Desirée?

9. In 1815, after fleeing to Rochefort, Napoleon surrendered to the captain of which battleship?

10. On which island did Napoleon die in 1821?

ANSWERS
1. Corsica 2. Stomach 3. Toulon 4. Waterloo 5. Shopkeepers 6. Buonaparte
7. Josephine Beauharnais 8. Marlon Brando 9. *Bellerophon* 10. St Helena

The Life and Times of Superman

Superman first appeared in Action Comics in 1938 and went on to become the subject of several films, several TV series, a radio series and a number of cartoon series. Below are ten super questions on the Man of Steel.

1. What name was Superman born with?
2. What is Clark Kent's job?
3. Which arch-enemy of Superman has been played on film by Gene Hackman?
4. What is the name of the home planet of Superman?
5. Which actor played the super-villain Zod in the Superman films?
6. In the TV series, *The New Adventures Of Superman*, Dean Cain plays our hero. Which actress plays Lois Lane?
7. In which town did Superman live as a young boy?
8. Who played the Man of Steel in the 1950s TV series?
9. Who, with Joe Shuster, was the co-creator of Superman?
10. What is the name of the editor of the Daily Planet?

ANSWERS
1. Kal-El 2. A newspaper reporter 3. Lex Luthor 4. Krypton 5. Terence Stamp 6. Teri Hatcher 7. Smallville 8. George Reeves 9. Jerry Siegel 10. Perry White

The Life and Times of Marilyn Monroe

Marilyn Monroe was born Norma Jean Baker in 1926 and made her movie début in a 1948 film called _Scudda Hoo, Scudda Hay_. Below are ten teasers on the life of the movie icon that is Marilyn Monroe.

1. In which 1959 Billy Wilder comedy did Marilyn share a screen kiss with Tony Curtis?

2. What was the title of the 1955 film that featured a memorable scene in which Marilyn's skirt was blown above her waist?

3. Which playwright was Marilyn's third husband?

4. What was the title of Marilyn's last film, which also saw the screen farewell of Clark Gable?

5. In which film did Marilyn sing the song 'Old Black Magic'?

6. What was the title of the film in which she co-starred with Betty Grable and Lauren Bacall?

7. The birth and death of Marilyn were recorded in which city?

8. Marilyn's second husband Joe di Maggio played baseball for which team?

9. In which film did Marilyn sing 'Diamonds Are A Girl's Best Friend'?

10. In what year did Marilyn die?

ANSWERS
1. _Some Like It Hot_ 2. _The Seven Year Itch_ 3. Arthur Miller 4. _The Misfits_ 5. _Bus Stop_ 6. _How To Marry A Millionaire_ 7. Los Angeles 8. New York Yankees 9. _Gentlemen Prefer Blondes_ 10. 1962

The Life and Times of King Arthur

King Arthur, the legendary King, held court in the kingdom of Camelot with his Knights of the Round Table. Below is a montage of mystical questions and answers on the legend of King Arthur.

1. Guinevere, the wife of Arthur, is said to have had an adulterous affair with which knight?

2. What was the name of King Arthur's shield?

3. Who played Arthur in the film, *Monty Python and the Holy Grail*?

4. Where was Arthur's sword Excalibur forged?

5. What is the name of the evil half-sister of King Arthur?

6. Who played King Arthur in the 1967 musical, *Camelot*?

7. What is the name of Arthur's father?

8. Who was the son of Sir Lancelot?

9. Was Cabal the name of Arthur's cat, dog or horse?

10. Which Hollywood star played Sir Lancelot in the film, *First Knight*?

ANSWERS

1. Sir Lancelot 2. Pridwen 3. Graham Chapman 4. Avalon 5. Morgan le Fay 6. Richard Harris 7. Uther Pendragon 8. Sir Galahad 9. His dog 10. Richard Gere

SESSION 6

The Life and Times of Mark Twain

American author Mark Twain was born in 1835 and is best remembered for his literary creations, Tom Sawyer and Huckleberry Finn. Test your literary logic with the ten questions below on the life of Mark Twain.

1. Which comet passed over Earth in the year Twain was born and next passed over the day before Twain died?
2. What is the name of Tom Sawyer's girlfriend?
3. What was Mark Twain's real name?
4. Which fantasy novel by Twain told the story of a man called Hank Morgan, who is knocked unconscious and awakens in King Arthur's England in AD538?
5. In which state of the USA were the adventures of Tom Sawyer and Huckleberry Finn set?
6. Which Twain novel tells of real-life events of 1547 concerning Prince Edward VI and Tom Canty?
7. Mark Twain's first published book contained the name of a creature in the title. Was this creature a frog, a ferret or a fox?
8. What is the name of the aunt that Tom Sawyer lives with?
9. What is the name of the runaway slave that is befriended by Huckleberry Finn?
10. What language did Twain describe as awful in his book, *A Tramp Abroad*?

ANSWERS

1. Halley's Comet 2. Becky Thatcher 3. Samuel L Clemens 4. *A Connecticut Yankee In King Arthur's Court* 5. Mississippi 6. *The Prince And The Pauper* 7. Frog – the book was entitled *The Celebrated Jumping Frog Of Calaveras* 8. Aunt Polly 9. Jim 10. German

The Life and Times of Simon & Garfunkel

The folk-rooted musical duo of Simon & Garfunkel first performed together in the 1950s. Below is a musical medley of questions on their life as a duo and as solo artists.

1. Which actress did Paul Simon marry in August 1983?

2. Which Simon & Garfunkel tune was covered by the girl band the Bangles in 1988?

3. What song did Paul Simon write whilst sitting on a railway station platform?

4. In which 1970 film based on a novel by Joseph Heller did Garfunkel play the character of Negley?

5. Simon & Garfunkel first charted in the USA under the name of which cartoon duo?

6. The Art Garfunkel song, 'Bright Eyes' featured in which animated film?

7. Which Hollywood actor featured in the video for the Paul Simon song, 'You Can Call Me Al'?

8. Which album by the duo was the best-selling album in the world in 1970?

9. The Simon & Garfunkel songs, 'Mrs Robinson' and 'The Sound Of Silence', featured in which film?

10. Which album by Paul Simon was named Record Of The Year at the 1988 Grammy Awards?

ANSWERS
1. Carrie Fisher 2. 'A Hazy Shade Of Winter' 3. 'Homeward Bound' 4. Catch 22 5. Tom & Jerry 6. Watership Down 7. Chevy Chase 8. Bridge Over Troubled Water 9. The Graduate 10. Graceland

6

The Life and Times of Eva Peron

Eva Peron was born in 1919 in a poverty-stricken family and went on to become the First Lady of Argentina. Below are ten questions on the life of the lady known as Evita.

1. What was the name of Eva's president husband?
2. Who wrote the lyrics for the stage musical, *Evita*?
3. What was Eva's surname at birth?
4. What was the name of the village in which Eva was born?
5. Which disease claimed the life of Eva Peron?
6. At the age of 14, Eva ran away to which city in her bid to become an actress?
7. In which European country was Eva's body buried under a false name?
8. Who played Che Guevara in the 1996 film, *Evita*?
9. What was the title of Eva Peron's autobiography?
10. In what year of the 1950s did Eva die?

The Life and Times of Bill Clinton

Bill Clinton was born on August 19, 1946 and became the 42nd president of the USA. Below are ten political posers on the life of Bill Clinton.

1. In 1978 Clinton became the governor of which US state?

2. What was the maiden name of his wife Hillary?

3. Who was Clinton's vice-president?

4. At which university did Clinton gain a law degree?

5. How many children do Bill and Hillary Clinton have?

6. What is the middle name of Bill Clinton?

7. Who did Clinton appoint as the first-ever female secretary of state of the USA?

8. In what year did Clinton give his first inaugural address as US president?

9. Bill Clinton became the first Democratic president to win a second term of office since whom?

10. Which former secretary of Clinton received a substantial financial pay-off after she accused him of having an extramarital affair with her?

ANSWERS

1. Arkansas 2. Rodham 3. Al Gore 4. Yale University 5. One – their daughter Chelsea 6. Jefferson 7. Madeleine Allbright 8. 1993 9. Franklin D Roosevelt 10. Gennifer Flowers

The Life and Times of Eddie Murphy

Eddie Murphy was born in 1961 and at 19 years of age joined the cast of *Saturday Night Live*, which provided a springboard for his leap into Hollywood films. Below are ten teasers on the life of Eddie Murphy.

1. What was the title of the 1996 film in which Murphy played seven different roles?
2. In which series of films did Eddie play a character called Axel Foley?
3. What was the title of the Disney film in which Murphy provided the voice of a dragon?
4. In which 1992 romantic comedy did he share a bedroom scene with Robyn Givens?
5. What was the title of the 1988 movie in which Eddie Murphy played an African tribal leader on a visit to the USA?
6. In which film, his first starring role, did Eddie play a wise-cracking convict called Reggie Hammond?
7. Which actor did Eddie trade places with in the film, *Trading Places*?
8. Who did Murphy co-star with in the film *Harlem Nights*, a man he described as his hero?
9. Is Eddie Murphy's middle name Wilson, Carter or Regan?
10. What connects Eddie Murphy with Rex Harrison and Hugh Lofting?

ANSWERS

1. The Nutty Professor 2. Beverly Hills Cop 3. Mulan 4. Boomerang 5. Coming To America 6. 48 Hours 7. Dan Aykroyd 8. Richard Pryor 9. Regan 10. Dr Doolittle; Rex Harrison first played the doctor on film, Lofting wrote the novel and Murphy played the doctor in a 1990s remake

The Life and Times of David Beckham

Football star David Beckham was born in 1975 and went on to captain England. Test your football facts with the ten questions below on the life of David Beckham.

1. What was his wife Victoria's maiden name?

2. In the 1998 World Cup, David was sent off against which country?

3. For which team did Beckham make his Football League début, whilst on loan from Manchester United?

4. In the 1996/97 season David scored a 60-yard lob against keeper Neil Sullivan. Who were Manchester United's opponents that day?

5. Which of the following is not a middle name of David Beckham. Is it Robert, George or Joseph?

6. What number of shirt did Beckham inherit from Eric Cantona?

7. What nickname is given to the Beckhams' palatial home?

8. Was David Beckham born in London, Liverpool or Manchester?

9. In what year did Beckham first captain England?

10. Against which country beginning with M did Beckham make his England début?

ANSWERS

1. Adams 2. Argentina 3. Preston North End 4. Wimbledon 5. George 6. Seven 7. Beckingham Palace 8. London 9. 2000 10. Moldova

6

The Life and Times of Hannibal Lecter

The insane criminal monster, Hannibal Lecter, first appeared in a novel entitled *Red Dragon* and became a household name following the film portrayal by Anthony Hopkins in *The Silence Of The Lambs*. Below are ten terrifying teasers on the life of Hannibal the cannibal.

1. Who directed the film, *The Silence Of The Lambs*?
2. What was the name of the serial killer that Hannibal helped Clarice Starling capture in *The Silence Of The Lambs*?
3. Which author created the character of Lecter?
4. Of which organisation is Clarice Starling a member?
5. What was the title of the 1986 film in which Lecter first featured on the big screen?
6. Who played Lecter in that film?
7. In *The Silence Of The Lambs* Lecter claimed to have washed down one of his victim's liver with what type of wine?
8. Who played the role of Clarice Starling in the 2001 film, *Hannibal*?
9. How many Oscars did *The Silence Of The Lambs* receive?
10. Which actor was fed his own brain by Lecter in the film *Hannibal*?

ANSWERS
1. Jonathan Demme 2. Buffalo Bill 3. Thomas Harris 4. FBI 5. *Manhunter* 6. Brian Cox 7. Chianti 8. Julianne Moore 9. Five 10. Ray Liotta

62

The Life and Times of Ludwig van Beethoven

The composer Beethoven was born in December 1770 and died in March 1827. Below are ten classical questions based on the life of Beethoven.

1. In which German city was Beethoven born?

2. Was Beethoven named Ludwig after his uncle, his father or his grandfather?

3. Which of the four seasons of the year is the alternative title for Beethoven's Violin Sonata in F?

4. Which composer, known as 'The father of the modern symphony', was an early tutor of Beethoven?

5. Who played Ludwig in the 1994 film, *Immortal Beloved*?

6. What was the title of Beethoven's only opera?

7. Was Beethoven six, seven or eight years old when he performed his first public concert?

8. Who wrote the song, 'Roll Over Beethoven'?

9. For which musical instrument did Beethoven compose the sonata entitled, 'Pathétique'?

10. In which Austrian city did Beethoven die?

ANSWERS
1. Bonn 2. Grandfather 3. Spring 4. Josef Haydn 5. Gary Oldman 6. *Fidelio* 7. Seven 8. Chuck Berry 9. Piano 10. Vienna

The Life and Times of Winston Churchill

Winston Churchill was born on November 30, 1874 and on his death he became the first-ever commoner to be granted a state funeral in Britain. Below are ten political posers on the statesman who led Great Britain during World War II.

1. In which palace was Winston Churchill born?

2. What was the name of Winston's father?

3. Who played Winston Churchill in the 1972 film, *Young Winston*?

4. In August 1940, Churchill said, 'Never in the field of human conflict was so much owed by so many to so few.' To which World War II battle was he referring?

5. In 1899, Churchill lost a by-election in Oldham whilst representing which party?

6. Which river was the subject of Churchill's book, *The River War*?

7. Three days after becoming prime minister Churchill gave a speech which included the words, 'I have nothing to offer but . . .' What four things did he offer?

8. As a young man was Churchill a keen footballer, polo player or golfer?

9. For which category did Churchill win a Nobel Prize?

10. In which year did Churchill die?

The Life and Times of Charles Schulz

Charles Schulz was born in Minnesota in 1922 and his death in February 2000 was mourned throughout the world. Below are ten posers on the creator of the *Peanuts* comic strip.

1. In which decade did the *Peanuts* comic strip first appear?

2. What is the name of Snoopy's master?

3. Which *Peanuts* character idolises the composer Beethoven?

4. What is the name of the yellow bird, best friend of Snoopy?

5. Was the family nickname of Charles Schulz, Speedy, Sparky or Spud?

6. What breed of dog is Snoopy?

7. What is the first name of the girl in the *Peanuts* strip whose last name is Van Pelt?

8. What is the middle name of Charles Schulz, which is also the surname of a female movie icon?

9. Who did Snoopy battle against when he transformed his kennel into a Sopwith Camel fighter plane?

10. Which *Peanuts* character continually sucks his thumb whilst clinging onto a security blanket?

ANSWERS

1. 1950s 2. Charlie Brown 3. Schroeder 4. Woodstock 5. Sparky – his uncle named him Sparky after a horse called Sparkplug in a comic strip called *Barney Google* 6. Beagle 7. Lucy 8. Monroe 9. The Red Baron 10. Linus

The Life and Times of the Addams Family

The Addams Family began life as a cartoon strip and was created by the American cartoonist Charles Addams. Below is an altogether kookie selection of creepy clues on the Addams Family.

1. What is the name of the wife of Gomez Addams?

2. Who did Ken Weatherwax play in the 1960s TV series?

3. Which of the following is not a cousin of the Addams Family? Cousin Cackle, Cousin Creep, Cousin Fungus, Cousin Gruesome or Cousin Grisly?

4. Who played Gomez Addams in the 1991 film version?

5. What is the name of the family's pet octopus?

6. What is the name of the character that consists of nothing but a hand?

7. Who played the butler, Lurch, in the 1960s TV series?

8. Which member of the Addams Family was played by Jackie Coogan on TV and Christopher Lloyd on film?

9. What was the full title of the 1993 film sequel?

10. Who played Wednesday Addams in the 1991 film?

ANSWERS

1. Morticia 2. Pugsley 3. Cousin Gruesome 4. Raul Julia 5. Aristotle 6. Thing 7. Ted Cassidy 8. Uncle Fester 9. *Addams Family Values* 10. Christina Ricci

The Life and Times of John McEnroe

Tennis star John McEnroe was born in 1959 and was first ranked No. 1 in the world in 1981. Below is a volley of tennis teasers on the man known as Superbrat.

1. In which European country was McEnroe born?
2. What was the name of the rock band that John formed with fellow tennis pro Pat Cash?
3. Is John McEnroe's middle name Patrick, Peter or Paul?
4. Which actress, daughter of the star of the film *Love Story*, did McEnroe marry and divorce?
5. How many times did John McEnroe win the US Open?
6. Who partnered John McEnroe for the majority of his doubles titles?
7. Is John McEnroe left- or right-handed?
8. Who did McEnroe beat in the final when gaining his first Wimbledon Singles title?
9. In which Wimbledon year did McEnroe call an umpire, 'The pits of the world' and exclaim, 'You cannot be serious'?
10. Which musician became McEnroe's second wife in 1997?

ANSWERS
1. Germany 2. Full Metal Rackets 3. Patrick 4. Tatum O'Neal 5. Four 6. Peter Fleming 7. Left-handed 8. Bjorn Borg 9. 1981 10. Patty Smyth

The Life and Times of Enid Blyton

Children's author Enid Blyton was born in London in 1897 and died in 1968. Below are ten novel questions on the creator of Noddy and the Famous Five.

1. In which town does Noddy live?

2. Was George, a member of the Famous Five, a boy or a girl?

3. What is the name of the Secret Seven's dog?

4. How many Famous Five stories did Blyton write – was it 11, 21 or 31?

5. Which intrepid gang of young investigators was led by Frederick Algernon Trotteville?

6. What is the name of Noddy's house?

7. How many legs in total did the Famous Five have between them?

8. Darrell Rivers and Sally Hope were pupils at which school created by Enid Blyton?

9. Who was the oldest member of the Famous Five?

10. Which of the following is not one of the members of the Secret Seven? Is it Pam, Colin, Susan, Janet, George, Jack, Peter or Barbara?

ANSWERS

1. Toytown 2. A girl, being short for Georgina 3. Scamper 4. 21 5. The Five Find-Outers 6. House For One 7. Twelve legs – eight human legs and four canine legs belonging to Timmy the dog 8. Mallory Towers 9. Julian 10. Susan

The Life and Times of Gilbert & Sullivan

The operatic duo Gilbert & Sullivan were born in 1836 and 1842 respectively and together composed 14 operas. Below is a medley of ten questions on the life of Gilbert & Sullivan.

1. Which opera featured three sisters called Yum-Yum, Pitti-Sing and Peep-Bo?
2. Which of the duo wrote the lyrics?
3. Which opera told the story of a fairy that married a mortal?
4. Which of their operas was sub-titled *The Slave Of Duty*?
5. Which opera set in a courtroom was the only one-act opera composed by Gilbert & Sullivan?
6. What are the first names of Gilbert & Sullivan?
7. Which of their operas opens in Venice in 1750?
8. How did Gilbert die in 1911?
9. What was the title of the 1999 Mike Leigh film that chronicled a chapter in the life of Gilbert & Sullivan?
10. Which Gilbert & Sullivan opera is sub-titled *The Lass That Loved A Sailor*?

ANSWERS
1. *The Mikado* 2. Gilbert 3. *Iolanthe* 4. *The Pirates Of Penzance* 5. *Trial By Jury* 6. William and Arthur 7. *The Gondoliers* 8. He died trying to save a drowning woman 9. *Topsy Turvy* 10. *HMS Pinafore*

The Life and Times of New York City

New York became the largest city of the USA in 1790 and in 1898 the newly adopted charter made it a metropolis of five boroughs. Below are ten questions on the history and landmarks of the city known as the Big Apple.

1. What was the original name of New York?
2. Which New York building saw the climax of the 1933 film, *King Kong*?
3. What is the name of the thoroughfare that is the centre of New York's advertising industry?
4. Which New York basketball team played its first league match in 1946?
5. Which museum in New York opened its doors to the public in 1959?
6. Which canal that opened in 1825 linked New York to the Great Lakes?
7. Who directed and starred in the 1979 film, *Manhattan*?
8. Which president accepted the Statue of Liberty on behalf of the USA?
9. Who was appointed mayor of New York in 2002?
10. Which island in New York was the principal federal immigration station of the USA from 1892 to 1954?

The Life and Times of Ford Cars

The Ford Motor Company was founded in 1903 by Henry Ford and ten investors. Below are ten questions on the history of Ford cars.

1. Which car was nicknamed the Tin Lizzie?

2. What model of Ford car did Steve McQueen drive in the 1968 film, *Bullit*?

3. In which city was the first Ford factory established?

4. Which model of Ford car was named after the son of Henry Ford?

5. The Henry Ford Museum in Dearborn is located in which US state?

6. Which model of Ford car was named after the venue of the 1956 Winter Olympics?

7. In which decade did Henry Ford die?

8. What was the model of the red-and-white Ford car driven by the TV cops Starsky & Hutch?

9. Which Ford model was named after an island found in the Bay of Naples?

10. On February 20, 2002, the last car rolled off the production line at which Ford plant in the county of Essex?

ANSWERS

1. Model T Ford 2. Ford Mustang 3. Detroit 4. Ford Edsel 5. Michigan 6. Ford Cortina 7. 1940s – he died in 1947 8. Ford Torino 9. Ford Capri 10. Dagenham

The Life and Times of John Travolta

The actor John Travolta was born in 1954 and made his big-screen début alongside William Shatner in the 1975 film, *The Devil's Rain*. **Below are ten movie mindbenders on the life of John Travolta.**

1. In which 1995 film did John co-star with Gene Hackman, Danny DeVito and Rene Russo?

2. What was the first film in which Travolta played the character of Tony Manero?

3. Which actress provided the love interest for Travolta in the film, *Look Who's Talking*?

4. In which 1996 film did John don a pair of angel's wings?

5. What was the title of the 1970s sitcom in which John Travolta played a student taught by a teacher called Kotter?

6. In which 1998 film did John portray a presidential candidate who was said to be based on Bill Clinton?

7. What was the name of the character played by Travolta in the film, *Grease*?

8. In which 1997 action thriller did John Travolta and Nicolas Cage exchange identities?

9. Which 1998 war film co-starred John Travolta, Nick Nolte, Sean Penn and Woody Harrelson?

10. In which Quentin Tarantino film did Travolta play the character of Vincent Vega?

ANSWERS
1. Get Shorty 2. Saturday Night Fever 3. Kirstie Alley 4. Michael 5. Welcome Back Kotter 6. Primary Colors 7. Danny Zuko 8. Face Off 9. The Thin Red Line 10. Pulp Fiction

The Life and Times of Mike Tyson

The boxer Mike Tyson was born in 1966 and turned professional in 1985, winning his first fifteen bouts by knockout. Below is a round of pugilistic posers on the life of Iron Mike Tyson.

1. How old was Tyson when he won his first world title?

2. Which boxer's thigh did Tyson bite during a press conference in January 2002?

3. Who did Tyson beat to take the WBC world title and in doing so became the youngest-ever Heavyweight World Champion?

4. Which trainer became the legal guardian of Mike Tyson on his 18th birthday?

5. To what religion did Mike Tyson convert whilst he was serving his prison sentence?

6. In 1990 who inflicted a shock defeat on Tyson in a world title fight?

7. In what year of the 1990s did Tyson receive a six-year jail sentence?

8. Is Mike Tyson's middle name Gerard, George or Graham?

9. Whose ear did Tyson bite in a 1997 world title fight?

10. Who did Tyson out-point in August 1987 to unify the world titles and become undisputed World Champion?

ANSWERS

1. 20 2. Lennox Lewis 3. Trevor Berbick 4. Cus D'Amato 5. Islam 6. James Buster Douglas 7. 1992 8. Gerard 9. Evander Holyfield 10. Tony Tucker

The Life and Times of Peter Pan

The story of Peter Pan first appeared as a stage play in 1904 at the Duke of York's Theatre in London. Below are ten trivia teasers on the boy that never grew up.

1. Which author created the character of Peter Pan?
2. According to Peter Pan what are the two things that are required to enable a person to fly?
3. What is the name of Captain Hook's ship?
4. What is the surname of the children that Peter took with him to Never Never Land?
5. In 1929, which hospital was granted the royalty rights to the novel, *Peter Pan*?
6. What is the name of the Newfoundland dog in the novel, *Peter Pan*?
7. Who played Tinkerbell in the film, *Hook*?
8. What is the name of the gang of children that live in Never Never Land and are said to have fallen out of their prams when they were young?
9. What is the name of the Indian princess heroically rescued by Peter Pan?
10. Which girl's name was specifically created by the author for the novel *Peter Pan*?

ANSWERS
1. JM Barrie 2. A little fairy dust and think a happy thought 3. *Jolly Roger* 4. Darling 5. Great Ormond Street Hospital 6. Nana 7. Julia Roberts 8. The Lost Boys 9. Tiger Lily 10. Wendy

The Life and Times of the Jacksons

The singing Jackson family began life as a trio in 1963 and became the Jackson 5 when Michael and Marlon joined the line-up. Below is a musical montage of trivia on the life of the Jacksons.

1. In 1984, Michael Jackson set his hair on fire whilst filming an advert for which soft drinks giant?

2. Under what name do Michael Jackson's nephews, Tito, Taryll and Tariano perform?

3. In 1970, which song became the Jacksons' first No. 1 when it topped the US charts for four weeks?

4. Which song was Michael performing at the 1996 Brit Awards when Jarvis Cocker, the lead singer with Pulp, invaded the stage?

5. Which of the Jackson family starred in the TV series *Diff'rent Strokes* and *Fame*?

6. With whom did Michael duet on the song 'Say, Say, Say'?

7. Who did Michael marry in May 1994?

8. Which of the Jackson clan had a solo hit with 'Let's Get Serious'?

9. What was the title of the film that starred Michael in 1998?

10. The actor Eddie Murphy and the model Iman starred in the video for which Michael Jackson song?

The Life and Times of Captain James Cook

Captain Cook was born in 1728 and joined the Royal Navy in 1755 as an ordinary seaman. Below is a selection of seafaring teasers on the life of Captain James Cook.

1. In 1771, Cook became the first commander of a ship to serve his crew fruit in combating which disease?

2. In which county was Captain Cook born?

3. What was the name of the ship in which Cook embarked on his first voyage around the world?

4. During which war that began in 1756 was Cook sent to map the estuary of the St Lawrence Seaway?

5. In 1770, which bay was renamed by Cook after the discovery of a large number of unknown plants?

6. What is the modern-day name for the Sandwich Islands, where Captain Cook met his death at the hands of natives?

7. What was the name of Cook's flagship on his second voyage around the world?

8. What device invented by John Harrison enabled Cook to determine the exact time of day and his ship's position on his voyages?

9. In 1770, Cook discovered and charted the east coast of Australia, which he claimed for Britain. What did Cook name this area?

10. Did Captain James Cook die in 1778, 1779 or 1780?

ANSWERS

1. Scurvy 2. Yorkshire, in a small village called Marton 3. *Endeavour* 4. The Seven Years' War 5. Botany Bay, which he originally called Stingray Bay 6. Hawaii 7. *Resolution* 8. A sea clock called a chronometer 9. New South Wales 10. 1779

The Life and Times of the Flintstones

The Stone Age family, the Flintstones, made their TV debut in the USA in 1960. Below are ten prehistoric posers on the residents of Bedrock in Cobblestone County.

1. What is the name of the Flintstones' daughter?

2. Who played Barney Rubble in the 1984 film?

3. What is Fred Flintstone's place of work?

4. What is the name of the Flintstones' prehistoric family pet?

5. What is Fred & Barney's favourite sport?

6. On what road do the Flintstones live?

7. What is the name of the Rubbles' baby son?

8. What was the maiden name of Wilma Flintstone?

9. Who played Betty Rubble in the 1994 film?

10. What is the name of the daily newspaper that Fred reads?

ANSWERS
1. Pebbles 2. Rick Moranis 3. Rock Head and Quarry Cave Construction Company
4. Dino 5. Ten-pin bowling 6. Stone Cave Road 7. Bam Bam 8. Wilma Slaghoople
9. Rosie O'Donnell 10. Daily Slate

8

The Life and Times of John Wayne

John Wayne was born in 1907 and made his big-screen debut in the 1927 film *The Drop Kick*. Below is a posse of posers on the life of the all-American actor John Wayne.

1. What first name was John Wayne born with?
2. Which leader was portrayed by John Wayne in the 1955 film, *The Conqueror*?
3. Which 1968 film directed by Wayne was made in a bid to gain support for America's involvement in the Vietnam War?
4. What was the name of John Wayne's pet dog that he owned as a teenager?
5. Which British pop group took their name from the title of a 1956 western starring John Wayne?
6. What was the only film for which John Wayne won a Best Actor Oscar?
7. Which member of the Rat Pack played John's brother in the film, *The Sons Of Katie Elder*?
8. Which 1949 film earned John Wayne his first Oscar nomination?
9. Name the three films starring John Wayne that contain the word Rio in the title.
10. Which 1976 film marked the screen farewell of John Wayne?

The Life and Times of the Olympic Games

French aristocrat Baron Pierre de Coubertin instigated the modern Olympics in 1896. Below is an athletic contest of questions and answers on the games.

1. Who scored seven perfect 10s on her way to collecting three gold medals at the 1976 Olympics?

2. At the 1992 games which European nation competed under one flag for the first time since 1964?

3. What was the venue of the 1994 Winter Olympics?

4. Which Canadian sprinter set a new world record when winning a gold medal in the 100 metres at the 1996 Atlanta Olympics?

5. Name the man who won a 1968 gold medal for the high jump and gave his name to a revolutionary style of jumping.

6. Which 1981 film that saw Ben Cross playing Harold Abrahams climaxed at the 1924 Paris Olympics?

7. Which US athlete won the eighth Olympic gold of his career at the 1992 games?

8. At the 1972 games, who won seven gold medals, all in world record times?

9. In which year of the 20th century were the Olympics held 2,240 metres (7,349 feet) above sea level?

10. In the 20th century which nation won the greatest number of medals at the Winter Olympics?

ANSWERS
1. Nadia Comaneci 2. Germany 3. Lillehammer 4. Donovan Bailey 5. Dick Fosbury 6. *Chariots Of Fire* 7. Carl Lewis 8. Mark Spitz 9. 1968 in Mexico City 10. Norway

The Life and Times of Rudyard Kipling

The writer Rudyard Kipling was born in 1865, won the Nobel Prize for Literature in 1907 and died in 1936. Test your literary logic with the ten questions below on the life of Rudyard Kipling.

1. In which 1975 film based on a Kipling novel did Christopher Plummer play Rudyard Kipling?

2. Which novel written in 1901 told the story of Kimball O'Hara who worked for the British Secret Service?

3. In which Indian city was Kipling born?

4. In which war was Kipling's son John killed in action?

5. What is the name of the collection of Kipling poems that includes in their number the poem, 'Gunga Din'?

6. What kind of bird is Mao in the Kipling novel, *The Jungle Book*?

7. In which building is Rudyard Kipling buried?

8. Did Rudyard Kipling ever receive a knighthood?

9. Which Kipling poem includes the words, 'and never the twain shall meet'?

10. What was the name of the panther in *The Jungle Book*?

ANSWERS
1. *The Man Who Would Be King* 2. *Kim* 3. Bombay 4. World War 1 5. *Barrack-Room Ballads* 6. A peacock 7. Westminster Abbey in Poets' Corner 8. No, he was twice offered the award in 1899 and 1903 but refused it on both occasions 9. 'The Ballad of East and West' 10. Bagheera

The Life and Times of Phil Collins

Phil Collins was born in 1951 in London and has enjoyed chart success as a member of the band Genesis and as a solo artist. Below are ten questions on the life of Phil Collins.

1. Who did Collins replace as lead vocalist with Genesis?

2. In 1983 Phil had a hit record on both sides of the Atlantic with a cover version of which Supremes classic?

3. As a teenager who did Collins play in a London stage production of *Oliver*?

4. In 1978 Genesis released the album *And Then There Were Three*. Who were the other two band members with Collins?

5. In which 1988 film did Collins play one of the great train robbers?

6. Which member of the band Earth, Wind and Fire duetted with Phil Collins on the 1985 hit 'Easy Lover'?

7. Which album earned Collins a Grammy Award for Album Of The Year in 1986?

8. In which US police TV drama did Collins play a game-show host called Phil the Shill?

9. Which Phil Collins hit, a trans-Atlantic chart-topper in 1988, was originally recorded by the Mindbenders?

10. Which album, featuring the track, 'Another Day In Paradise', reached No. 1 in the charts in both the USA and the UK?

ANSWERS
1. Peter Gabriel 2. 'You Can't Hurry Love' 3. The Artful Dodger 4. Mike Rutherford and Tony Banks 5. Buster 6. Philip Bailey 7. No Jacket Required 8. Miami Vice 9. 'A Groovy Kind Of Love' 10. But Seriously

The Life and Times of the White House

The building of the White House began in 1792 and was completed in 1800. George Washington conceived it although he never actually lived in the building. Below are ten political posers of the history and occupants of the White House.

1. Which office of the White House was added to the building in 1909?

2. Standing on Pennsylvania Avenue, what is the number of the White House?

3. Which TV series starring Martin Sheen gives a dramatised account of White House activities?

4. Who was the first president to own an official White House car?

5. Who was the first US president to live in the White House?

6. In 1899, Benjamin Harrison became the first president to bring what kind of tree into the White House?

7. Are there 112, 122 or 132 rooms in the White House?

8. What was the title of the film co-starring Will Smith and Jeff Goldblum that saw the White House being destroyed by alien invaders?

9. Who is the only President to have been married in a wedding ceremony held at the White House?

10. Why did President Woodrow Wilson introduce a flock of sheep to the White House lawn?

ANSWERS

1. The Oval Office 2. 1600 3. *The West Wing* 4. William Taft 5. John Adams, the second US president, was the first to live in the White House 6. Christmas tree 7. 132 8. *Independence Day* 9. Grover Cleveland 10. Wilson brought a flock of sheep to the lawn to assist the war effort during World War I. The grazing sheep saved manpower by cutting the grass and also earned £50,000 for the Red Cross when their wool was auctioned.

The Life and Times of Star Trek

Star Trek the TV series, began on American TV in 1966, and in 1979 the first of several films, *Star Trek The Motion Picture*, was released. Below are ten Trekkie teasers for your enjoyment.

1. Who is the creator of Star Trek?

2. Who played Pavel Chekov in the TV show?

3. Which former singer for Duke Ellington played Lieutenant Uhuru?

4. What was the sub-title of the third Star Trek movie?

5. Who was the first captain of the USS *Enterprise*, who appeared in the pilot show for the TV series?

6. Who, played by Patrick Stewart, captained the *Enterprise* in the TV series *Star Trek – The Next Generation*?

7. What was the name of Dr McCoy's nurse played by Majel Barrett?

8. Who plays Captain Jonathan Archer in the TV series *Enterprise*?

9. What type of crystals are used to power the engines of the *Enterprise*?

10. In which Star Trek TV series did Kate Mulgrew play Captain Kathryn Janeway?

ANSWERS

1. Gene Roddenberry 2. Walter Koenig 3. Nichelle Nichols 4. *The Search For Spock* 5. Captain Christopher Pike 6. Jean Luc Picard 7. Nurse Christine Chapel – Majel Barrett was the wife of Gene Roddenberry 8. Scott Bakula 9. Dilithium crystals 10. *Star Trek: Voyager*

The Life and Times of Michael Douglas

Hollywood superstar Michael Douglas was born in New Jersey in 1944, and followed in his father Kirk's footsteps to become an international film star. Below are ten questions on the life and films of Michael Douglas.

1. Which actress was fatally attracted to Michael in a 1987 film?

2. For which 1987 film did Douglas receive a Best Actor Oscar?

3. What was the title of the first film in which he co-starred with Catherine Zeta Jones?

4. In which 1989 film did Kathleen Turner play his wife and Danny DeVito his divorce lawyer?

5. In which psychological thriller did Douglas play an alcoholic cop investigating a writer played by Sharon Stone?

6. In which TV series did Michael Douglas play the character of Steve Keller?

7. In which 1980 film telling the story of a cover-up at a nuclear power station did Douglas co-star with Jack Lemmon?

8. Which Oscar-winning film starring Jack Nicholson did Michael Douglas co-produce?

9. What was the title of the 1994 film in which Demi Moore sexually harassed Michael?

10. What was the title of the first film in which he co-starred with Kathleen Turner and Danny DeVito?

ANSWERS
1. Glenn Close 2. Wall Street 3. Traffic 4. The War Of The Roses 5. Basic Instinct 6. The Streets Of San Francisco 7. The China Syndrome 8. One Flew Over The Cuckoo's Nest 9. Disclosure 10. Romancing The Stone

The Life and Times of the Grand National

The Grand National horse race was first contested in 1837 and was won by a horse called the Duke. Below are ten racy riddles on the history of the Grand National.

1. In 1839, the National was first contested at which Liverpool course?

2. Which horse recorded the first of three National victories in 1973?

3. At what long odds did Foinavon win the 1967 National?

4. Which National-winning horse was ridden by Bob Champion and featured in the film *Champions*?

5. In 1956, which horse owned by the Queen lost the race when it jumped a non-existent obstacle and slipped when approaching the winning line?

6. In 1983, who became the first woman to train the winner of the Grand National?

7. In 1977, who became the first woman to ride in the Grand National?

8. Where was the race contested from 1916 to 1918?

9. In what year of the 1990s was the National declared null and void due to a false start?

10. Was the Grand National fence called Valentine's named after a horse, a jockey or the saint?

ANSWERS

1. Aintree 2. Red Rum 3. 100-1 4. Aldaniti 5. Devon Loch 6. Jenny Pitman 7. Charlotte Brew 8. Gatwick 9. 1993 10. A horse. In 1840 a horse called Valentine reared up violently before the fence but still managed to negotiate it successfully.

SESSION 9

The Life and Times of H G Wells

H G Wells was born in Kent in 1866 and died in London in 1946. Test your literary logic with the ten questions below on the life of HG Wells.

1. Which novel penned by Wells in 1901 sees the heroes captured by ant-like creatures called Selenites?

2. Which Wells novel, his first major success, is set partly in the year 802701?

3. What was the title of the novel about a mad scientist that was first adapted into a film in 1933 starring Claude Rains?

4. Which sport did the father of HG Wells play professionally?

5. The musical *Half A Sixpence* was based on which novel by H G Wells?

6. Which book tells the story of a character called Prendick who visits an island inhabited by Beast People?

7. What does the HG stand for in the name of HG Wells?

8. Which author of the novel, *Journey To The Centre Of The Earth* once accused Wells of having 'scientifically implausible ideas'?

9. Prior to becoming a full-time writer was HG Wells a doctor, a teacher or a farmer?

10. Which novel opens with the line, 'No one would have believed in the last years of the nineteenth century that this world was being watched keenly and closely by intelligences greater than man's'?

ANSWERS
1. *First Men In The Moon* 2. *The Time Machine* 3. *The Invisible Man* 4. Cricket 5. *Kipps* 6. *The Island Of Dr Moreau* 7. Herbert George 8. Jules Verne 9. A teacher 10. *The War Of The Worlds*

The Life and Times of Cher

Cher was born on May 20, 1946 and is one of a select group of artists to have had a No. 1 hit and have won an Oscar. Below are ten trivia teasers on the life of Cher.

1. At 16 years of age Cher left home to live with which man 12 years her senior?

2. Who did Cher duet with on the 1981 hit, 'Dead Ringer For love'?

3. In which film did Winona Ryder play the daughter of Cher?

4. What was the title of the 1995 charity hit on which Cher collaborated with Eric Clapton, Chrissie Hynde and Neneh Cherry?

5. What is the name Cher short for?

6. What was the title of the 1987 film for which Cher won a Best Actress Oscar?

7. How old was Cher when the song 'I Got You Babe' first hit the charts?

8. Which rock star did Cher marry in 1975?

9. What was the title of the 1985 film in which Cher played the single mother of a teenager with a disfiguring bone disease?

10. Which song was a world-wide No. 1 hit for Cher in 1998?

ANSWERS
1. Sonny Bono 2. Meatloaf 3. *Mermaids* 4. 'Love Can Build A Bridge' 5. Cherilyn 6. *Moonstruck* 7. 19 8. Greg Allman 9. *Mask* 10. 'Believe'

The Life and Times of Butch Cassidy & The Sundance Kid

The Wild West outlaws Butch Cassidy & the Sundance Kid were memorably played on film in 1969 by Paul Newman and Robert Redford. Below are ten trivia teasers on the lives of Butch and Sundance.

1. What was the real first name of Butch Cassidy?

2. How did Butch Cassidy get his nickname of Butch?

3. What was the real first name of the Sundance Kid?

4. How did the Sundance Kid get his nickname?

5. Which song from the 1969 film about their lives won a Best Song Oscar?

6. According to that film, in which country did Butch & Sundance die a violent death?

7. What was the name of the prostitute who was the fiancée of the Sundance Kid?

8. Who directed the 1969 film, *Butch Cassidy & The Sundance Kid*?

9. What was the name of the gang that Butch formed in 1896 that later joined forces with the Hole in the Wall Gang?

10. Who played the title roles in the 1979 film, *Butch And Sundance: The Early Days*?

ANSWERS

1. Robert – he was called Robert Leroy Parker 2. Before turning to a life of crime he worked as a butcher in the state of Wyoming 3. Henry – he was called Henry Longbaugh 4. After serving 18 months in Sundance Jail, Wyoming for stealing a horse 5. 'Raindrops Keep Fallin' On My Head' 6. Bolivia 7. Etta Place, though in the 1969 film she was portrayed as a teacher 8. George Roy Hill 9. The Wild Bunch 10. Tom Berenger and William Katt

The Life and Times of Hanna Barbera

The American animators Hanna and Barbera were born in 1910 and 1911 respectively and in 1937 created *Tom & Jerry* for MGM. Below are ten questions on the life and cartoons of Hanna Barbera.

1. Which cartoon feline, the indisputable leader of the gang, was voiced by Arnold Stang?

2. Which cartoon canine's name was lifted from a line from the Frank Sinatra song 'Strangers In The Night'?

3. Which Hanna Barbera cartoon series was set in the year AD 3000?

4. Which cartoon told of the trials and tribulations of the Boyle family?

5. Which song was Huckleberry Hound often heard singing?

6. What was the name of the Park Ranger, the perpetual adversary of Yogi Bear?

7. What are the first names of Hanna and Barbera?

8. Which martial arts hero was accompanied by a striped cat called Spot?

9. What were the names of the two mice that continually tormented a cat called Mr Jinx?

10. Who was the only female driver in the Wacky Races?

ANSWERS

1. Top Cat 2. Scooby Doo 3. *The Jetsons* 4. *Wait Till Your Father Gets Home* 5. 'My Darling Clementine' 6. Ranger John Smith 7. William & Joseph 8. Hong Kong Phooey 9. Pixie and Dixie 10. Penelope Pitstop

The Life and Times of Harrison Ford

Harrison Ford was born in Chicago in 1942 and became an overnight star after his portrayal of Han Solo in *Star Wars*. Below is a trivia screen test on the life and films of Harrison Ford.

1. Which 1993 film saw Ford attempting to track down a one-armed killer?

2. In which film did Harrison Ford play a cop called John Book, who was forced to hide in an Amish community?

3. In which 1997 action thriller did he play the president of the USA?

4. Which 1982 sci-fi thriller saw Harrison hunting a robot played by Rutger Hauer?

5. Which CIA agent did Harrison Ford first play in the film, *Patriot Games*?

6. What was the title of the film that provided Ford's third outing as Indiana Jones?

7. Which screenwriter did Harrison marry in 1983?

8. In which 1990 film was Harrison Ford accused of the murder of Greta Scacchi?

9. In the 1987 film *Frantic*, Harrison Ford's wife was kidnapped in which capital city?

10. In which 1988 comedy drama did Ford co-star with Melanie Griffiths and Sigourney Weaver?

ANSWERS
1. The Fugitive 2. Witness 3. Air Force One 4. Bladerunner 5. Jack Ryan 6. Indiana Jones And The Last Crusade 7. Melissa Mathison 8. Presumed Innocent 9. Paris 10. Working Girl

The Life and Times of Diego Maradona

Footballing superstar Diego Maradona was born in October 1960 and in 1986 captained Argentina to World Cup glory. Test your football facts with the ten questions below on the life of Maradona.

1. Maradona was born in Lanus, a town just outside which city?

2. Which South American club bought Maradona from Argentinos Juniors for £1 million?

3. In how many World Cups did Maradona play?

4. In 1991 why was Maradona suspended for 15 months by FIFA?

5. How many goals did Maradona score in the 1986 World Cup finals?

6. Which Italian club did Maradona win two league titles with?

7. Which Spanish club signed Maradona for £5 million in 1982?

8. Was Maradona 16, 17 or 18 when he was first capped for Argentina?

9. Against which keeper did Maradona score the 'hand of God' goal in the 1986 World Cup?

10. What number shirt did Maradona wear when representing Argentina?

ANSWERS
1. Buenos Aires 2. Boca Juniors 3. Four 4. For testing positive for cocaine 5. Five 6. Napoli 7. Barcelona 8. 16 9. Peter Shilton 10. 10

The Life and Times of Hans Christian Andersen

Hans Christian Andersen was born in 1805 and began publishing fairytales in 1835. Test your literary logic with the ten questions below on the life of Hans Christian Andersen.

1. In 1828 Andersen passed his leaving exam at the University of which capital city?
2. What did the Ugly Duckling turn into?
3. What is the name of the Little Mermaid?
4. Which fairytale begins with the line, 'Once upon a time there was a woman whose only wish was to have a tiny little child'?
5. In which Danish city was Hans Christian Andersen born?
6. Did Andersen ever meet Charles Dickens?
7. Which singer known as the Swedish Nightingale did Hans fall in love with in 1843?
8. In which fairytale did a young boy exclaim, 'The Emperor is naked!'?
9. Which of the following was not a fairytale by Hans Christian Andersen. Is it *The Snow Queen*, *The Snowdrop* or *The Snow Princess*?
10. Who played the title role in the 1952 film, *Hans Christian Andersen*?

ANSWERS

1. Copenhagen 2. A beautiful swan 3. Ariel 4. *Thumbelina* 5. Odense 6. Yes, in 1857 on a visit to England he stayed at the house of Charles Dickens for one month 7. Jenny Lind 8. *The Emperor's New Clothes* 9. *The Snow Princess* 10. Danny Kaye

The Life and Times of Andrew Lloyd Webber

Andrew Lloyd Webber was born in 1948 and dropped out of Oxford University to pursue a career in music. Below is a tuneful trivia test on the life and works of Andrew Lloyd Webber.

1. Which Lloyd Webber stage musical featured the song, 'Music Of The Night'?

2. Which book by TS Eliot provided the inspiration for the musical, *Cats*?

3. Who did Andrew marry in 1984?

4. What is the name of the theatre company that Lloyd Webber founded in 1977?

5. What was the title of the first musical written by Lloyd Webber and Tim Rice that proved to be an abject failure?

6. Which musical that opened in 1984 saw the cast performing on roller skates?

7. What is the name of Andrew's cello-playing brother?

8. Which Lloyd Webber musical told the story of an ageing silent screen star called Norma Desmond?

9. Which musical featured 'King Herod's Song'?

10. Who wrote the lyrics for 'Whistle Down The Wind'?

ANSWERS
1. *Phantom Of The Opera* 2. *Old Possum's Book Of Practical Cats* 3. Sarah Brightman 4. The Really Useful Theatre Group 5. *The Likes Of Us* 6. *Starlight Express* 7. Julian 8. *Sunset Boulevard* 9. *Jesus Christ Superstar* 10. Jim Steinman

The Life and Times of the Three Musketeers

The novel *The Three Musketeers* was published in 1844 and has since inspired numerous Hollywood film productions. Below is a swashbuckling trivia test on the Three Musketeers.

1. Which author created *The Three Musketeers*?
2. Which king was served by the Musketeers?
3. What is a musket, after which they were named?
4. What was the title of the novel that concluded the epic adventures of the Musketeers?
5. To which city does D'Artagnan travel to in the opening chapter of *The Three Musketeers* novel?
6. Alphabetically who is the first of the Three Musketeers?
7. Is the character of Richelieu a cardinal, a duke or a judge?
8. Who played D'Artagnan in the 1993 film, *The Three Musketeers*?
9. Who played D'Artagnan in the 1973 film, *The Three Musketeers*?
10. Who played D'Artagnan in the 1948 film, *The Three Musketeers*?

ANSWERS

1. Alexandre Dumas 2. Louis XIII 3. A long and heavy matchlock firearm used in the 17th century 4. *The Man In The Iron Mask* 5. Paris 6. Aramis 7. A cardinal 8. Chris O'Donnell 9. Michael York 10. Gene Kelly

The Life and Times of Disney films

Disney productions were the brainchild of Walt Disney and his character of Mickey Mouse first appeared in a 1928 animation called *Steamboat Willie*. Below is a selection of animated questions and answers on the wonderful world of Disney.

1. Which Disney cartoon featured the song 'Little April Showers' and was based on a novel by Felix Salten?

2. Ursula the Sea Witch was a character in which film?

3. Which Disney animation told the story of Princess Aurora?

4. *The Return of Jafar* is a sequel to which cartoon film?

5. What was the name of the snake that sang 'Trust In Me', in *The Jungle Book*?

6. What is the name of Simba's father in *The Lion King*?

7. Which Disney film featured a blissfully happy married couple called Anita and Roger Radcliff?

8. Which Disney duo enjoyed a romantic spaghetti dinner at a restaurant called Tony's?

9. In which film did a pair of intrepid rodent heroes called Bianca and Bernard first appear?

10. Which Disney character sang the song, 'Whistle While You Work'?

ANSWERS
1. *Bambi* 2. *The Little Mermaid* 3. *Sleeping Beauty* 4. *Aladdin* 5. Kaa 6. Mufasa 7. *101 Dalmatians* 8. *Lady and the Tramp* 9. *The Rescuers* 10. Snow White